G000123302

A GIRL CALLED

FRED

A GIRL CALLED

FRED

ROGER WILLGOOSE

Copyright © 2014 Roger Willgoose

The moral right of the author has been asserted.

Apart from any fair dealing for the purposes of research or private study,
or criticism or review, as permitted under the Copyright, Designs and Patents
Act 1988, this publication may only be reproduced, stored or transmitted, in
any form or by any means, with the prior permission in writing of the
publishers, or in the case of reprographic reproduction in accordance with
the terms of licences issued by the Copyright Licensing Agency. Enquiries
concerning reproduction outside those terms should be sent to the publishers.

Matador
9 Priory Business Park
Kibworth Beauchamp
Leicestershire LE8 0RX, UK
Tel: (+44) 116 279 2299
Fax: (+44) 116 279 2277
Email: books@troubador.co.uk
Web: www.troubador.co.uk/matador

ISBN 978 1783063 635

British Library Cataloguing in Publication Data.
A catalogue record for this book is available from the British Library.

Typeset in Book Antiqua by Troubador Publishing Ltd
Printed and bound in the UK by TJ International, Padstow, Cornwall

Matador is an imprint of Troubador Publishing Ltd

*This book is dedicated to the memory of my husband,
the author, who died in 2010.*

*A kind, caring and generous man, Roger had a
wonderful sense of humour and was well liked by all
who knew him.*

*He would have been so proud to see his book
published and it is a suitable memorial to celebrate
his character, his generosity and his popularity. He
will always be remembered.*

Jean Willgoose

1

A New Home

The cigarette slowly smouldered away and I gave a sharp howl of pain as I hurriedly threw it into the fire and pushed a burnt index finger into my mouth. The two women in the room looked up sharply, one showing mild concern, the other grinning and calling me a 'twit'. I had been watching a small dog with black and tan hair snuffling and nosing its way around the room, carefully exploring every corner and piece of furniture.

From time to time the little dog stopped and, ears pricked, glared at a black cat sitting on the knee of one of the women. The cat glared back and spat but seemed disinclined to move from its position of safety. The dog continued exploring.

"I think," began the woman with the cat, "that they had better be, er, introduced." This was my wife Jean, the one who had laughed and called me a 'twit' when I had burned my finger on the cigarette. Sitting beside her was her aunt, also Jean. The Yorkshire terrier inspecting the house was called Acol and, although I didn't fully agree with what was happening, Acol was in the process of being adopted into a new home. The part I didn't agree with was that it was my home which was doing the adopting.

The whole affair had started some weeks ago at a wedding. The three of us had been invited to attend the ceremony and, during the compulsory booze up that followed, Auntie Jean remarked that she was in a dilemma over her pet dog. It seemed that she had moved to a new job carrying no little responsibility and one which could on occasion keep her away from home for fairly long periods. The problem was Acol, her six-year-old Yorkshire terrier bitch. Auntie Jean did not feel that she could leave the dog alone for long periods and was desperately seeking a new home for her where she knew she would be kindly treated.

Now Jean is a sucker for hard luck stories particularly if they concern animals. She won't eat rabbit pie on the grounds that her friend, who lives three doors away from us, keeps pet rabbits in a hutch in the back garden. This may seem strange, but she does not altogether trust me concerning rabbits and small game and will not take the risk that she may have been stroking her supper a few days before. The reason she does not trust me may become apparent later so, as they say in the books – read on.

I began to get worried as my wife became progressively interested in the future of the animal under discussion and was about to interrupt with an argument along the lines that, while we sympathised

2

with Auntie Jean's predicament, we could not possibly give the unfortunate animal a home because of our cat, when Jean launched, what I believe they call, a pre-emptive strike.

"Right then," she beamed, giving me a quick elbow in the ribs, "we'll have her." The elbow had winded me slightly and, before I could get my bit in about the cat, Auntie Jean had smiled her thanks and said that of course there would be no charge which, under the circumstances, I thought was bloody cheeky. Looking back, and knowing what I do now, I suppose I would cheerfully have parted with a few hundred quid but at the time it seemed a bit much.

We had the row after the wedding reception had finally broken up and Auntie Jean was speeding her way back to Yorkshire, safe in the knowledge that a new home had been found for Acol. I should have had more sense than to protest there and then because I could see that Jean was gunned up and waiting. As it turned out I got the works, from "How could you refuse the little mite a home?" to "It's people like you who start wars." Tears followed and Jean knows I can't stand to see her crying, so we called a truce and I said I would think it over.

The following day was Sunday and breakfast had barely been cleared away before Jean started the softening up process. She began by recalling her childhood and bemoaning the fact that she had never been allowed to own a dog. A cat yes, but after all we had our black cat Jinx. But a dog would be an ideal

3

friend for… and here she played her trump card… our four-year-old son Stephen, who was by this time taking a deep interest in this one sided conversation. Steve has always been a bright lad and it didn't take him long to catch the general drift of Jean's argument and the thought of a dog for a pal put him firmly on her side. As a last resort I reminded them both of Jinx's 'condition'.

Jinxie was due to have kittens anytime in the next day or two. She was a rather beautiful cat really, I suppose, although I can't say I am over fond of cats at the best of times. Anyhow, her slim dark figure obviously appealed to the local tom cats as had become apparent one wet evening a few weeks before.

Jinx always liked to wander about the neighbourhood particularly after dark. One night, as we were about to lock up and go to bed, the comparative stillness was broken by the yowling screams of what passes for feline lovemaking. By the light of the street lamps through the teeming rain we saw Jinx and a scruffy grey moggy, which had been hanging around for a few days, disappearing under a Ford Cortina parked across the lane. Jean dashed out into the night and, kneeling beside the car, implored Jinx to stop whatever it was she was doing, at the same time casting grave doubts on the parentage of the other participant in the affair. I was of the opinion that they were rather clever to get out of the rain and, from the shelter of our back doorway, I listened to Jean's running commentary on the activity under the car which, by the sound of it, was reaching some sort of climax.

4

"Come out, come out you filthy pair," howled Jean, now almost wet through.

"Can't stop nature, love," I called from the doorway by way of help.

"Don't encourage 'em," came back the reply, "they don't need it." The rain pelted down and the screeching from underneath and beside the car subsided slowly.

My defeated and rain–bedraggled wife slowly walked down the path. "Fat lot of help you were," she glowered.

"Very difficult to stop when it gets to an advanced stage, love," I replied.

Presently Jinx strolled sedately down the path arching her back and purring softly to be met with a hail of abuse from Jean. Jinx ignored her – she ignored practically everybody anyway – and slid into her little cat house beside the back doorstep. She was safe there; nobody could get at her there. Steve had tried once and had been rewarded with four bright stripes oozing blood down his forearm.

So we were saddled with a pregnant cat and, the way things looked now, we were about to have a Yorkshire terrier unloaded upon us, to complicate matters even further. It was one of Jean's quicker conquests. I capitulated, after about an hour of intensive pressure from wife and son, with the sneaking thought that the dog might sort Jinx out a bit.

You may have gathered that Jinx and I didn't get along too well. When I'm not watching football or playing snooker or being led into bad ways by my mates, I spend quite a lot of my spare time growing vegetables in a couple of gardens I look after. The seed beds are at home and Jinx was under the misconception that they had been specially prepared solely as areas where she could dig and defecate as the mood took her. Of course this was not so, a fact of which she was constantly being reminded by the toe of my boot.

Jean called me a cruel and unfeeling swine but continued to cook, and eat with relish, such vegetable produce as managed to survive Jinx's bowel and bladder functions. I thought this attitude of Jean's rather unjust but, much as I love her, I have long given up hope of ever fully understanding exactly what goes on under that cap of fair hair. Being a teacher, Jean is not exactly unintelligent but, apart from being a rather brilliant mathematician, it seems to me sometimes that her views on logic are rather indistinct when applied to everyday things.

Jinx duly produced three kittens much to the delight of Jean and the amazement of Stephen who, not being a witness at the birth, began to ask some pertinent questions as to their origin. Jean patiently informed the inquiring four-year-old that they had 'grown in Jinx's tummy and then popped out'. With that directness and honesty so sadly lacking in the majority of adults, Steve began to go into more detail, and Jean hurriedly changed the subject as he asked exactly how the 'popping out' had occurred.

Jinx nursed the kittens with more affection than she had ever showed to anyone or anything before, except perhaps for the scruffy grey tom cat under the Ford. Maybe that is not strictly true as Jean also had a place in Jinx's affections perhaps because the cat realised that, while she was tolerated by Steve (he hadn't forgotten the scratches) and me, Jean loved the little black creature that deigned to live with us. While Jinx would grudgingly permit Steve and me to inspect and admire the kittens, she positively crooned as Jean fed her and generally fussed over her family.

It was into this situation that on one bright crisp autumn morning Auntie Jean arrived to spend the weekend accompanied by, what looked like at first sight, a yard brush with ears. Jinx took one look at the visitors coming down the path and promptly retreated to the kittens which were in their box in the hall, safely out of harm's way. We thought they were out of harm's way but Jinx obviously didn't as, while we were occupied with greeting our visitors, she surreptitiously removed all three to the safety of the garage. It took Jean two hours to find them afterwards.

Acol hopped over the kitchen doorstep and glanced around as the two Jeans flung their arms around each other before we all trooped into the house, Auntie Jean calling Acol to follow. Steve and I looked at the dog.

"It's not very big, Daddy, is it?" remarked Steve.

'It' as he put it was not very big but, to my relief, it was not so small either; certainly not one of those tiny creatures with floor length hair that parade up and down the show ring at Crufts. I had harboured a hidden dread that we were to be lumbered with a squeaking beribboned lap dog, but I need not have worried. She looked more like a pirate than a show ring champion although, as we subsequently found out, her bloodline was a damn sight bluer in Yorkshire terrier circles than many of the pretentious pampered Yorkies that nervously twitch and snap their way through life as child substitutes.

The piratical aspect owed much to the fact that Acol had only one eye. One eye that worked that is. Her right eye was covered with a hard scale. We found out later that she had been born with an inverted eyelid but, as it caused her no pain, a succession of veterinary surgeons had declined to operate. The other eye held a bright brown clearness that took in all around her. I had a sneaking feeling that she was observing us more than we were inspecting her. She snuffled her way around the house, ignoring everyone, as Jinx slinked into the room and gracefully leapt on Jean's lap.

That was when I burnt my finger on the cigarette and Jean said that dog and cat should be introduced.

Top Dog

In any relationship the introductory period forms an extremely important part. It is a time of assessment for both parties, each of the other. While opinions formed at this time may be subsequently modified or even totally contradicted, it is a time when snap decisions are made and promptly acted upon so that the relationship may continue along whatever lines the adopted opinions indicate. At least that's what a friend of mine called Harry keeps telling me. Harry spends his time drinking lots of beer and when he isn't drinking beer he listens to other people talk and then tells them exactly what he thinks of them. What's more he gets paid a lot of money for doing it, but the people have to lie down on a couch while the talking is going on. He doesn't drink beer while he is talking to these people, as he says that they wouldn't come to see him if he did, but he does at all other times. I have been after Harry's job for the last twelve years.

Acol and Jinx decided to fight, having taken a full

millisecond to size up each other. The encounter was inconclusive as they were promptly seized and admonished by their respective owners amid much cheering on from Steve, who seemed rather disappointed at the abrupt enforced cessation of hostilities. I observed that holding them nose to nose was a rather daft thing to do but, as I was immediately shouted down by the other three, I decided that henceforth silence was my best ally.

Jinx slunk away to her kittens and the dog continued her exploratory sniffing around the house while Auntie Jean unpacked her suitcase and prepared for what proved a rather pleasant weekend.

Now Auntie Jean is a thoroughly good sort. She is clever and witty without being malicious in any way and makes altogether good company. She is also an accomplished bridge player and has indeed competed at the highest level: once in the same company as Omar Sharif (the star of Dr Zhivago) and this is where the name Acol came from. Apparently it is a term used in the game. As I know less about bridge than I do about atomic physics, and I know sod all about that, the significance left me totally unimpressed.

However, it seemed that Acol had a small claim to fame as one of her last litter of puppies had been sold to the President of Nicaragua. This came out during the evening as we sat beside the fire after having packed Steve off to bed Jean firmly promising him, with a worried glance in my direction, that the dog could stay. She certainly wasn't going to get any strong objections from me. I know when I'm licked, but it does no harm to promote a little air of uncertainty as it sometimes comes in handy when conditions are being laid down, as usually happens at our home. Of course those conditions are rapidly forgotten as the situation finds its own level, but I always like to feel that if I've been conned, I have at least had some say in the matter. It's called vanity.

Auntie Jean wasn't quite sure of the whereabouts of Nicaragua, but this problem was solved when Jean triumphantly informed us all that it was in Central Africa. Jean may produce mathematical geniuses at her school but God help them if they venture more than a few yards away from their front doors. After all, when you are taught as a child that Bradford is on the left side of Leeds as you look up, what chance have you got at Spaghetti Junction?

I read some time ago that the President of Nicaragua had been overthrown in a coup. I'm not surprised as, if his geography was as good as Jean's, he was living in the wrong continent anyway,

"It's them bloody Africans you know," said Jean one day years later, nodding sagely over the newspaper account of the President's downfall. But we can't help but wonder sometimes what happened to the little dog.

After a couple of hours of frantic searching we had the kittens safely back in their box in the hall. During the search Acol was tied up so that any contribution that she felt inclined to make would not lead to a bloodbath. Jinx had a good time playing a sort of hunt the slipper game with us as the mugs, and emitting feline sniggers each time she passed the tied up Yorkie.

Of course the animosity of cat and dog was a problem and, as we sat talking about it, I thought at one stage that Auntie Jean would be reluctant to leave Acol with us. But Jean began making wild promises about Jinx's good behaviour and then they decided on a trial period of a month. After that time, if the two didn't get on or Acol pined too much, the deal was off and the dog went back to Yorkshire.

Now Jean is, what I believe is called in the best of circles, a very determined lady. I think that it's a nice way of saying that she's as stubborn as a mule, but then I don't move in the best of circles. In the case of Acol Jean was determined to succeed. I can always tell when she is determined as the end of her nose wobbles up and down when she talks, and that night it was going like a road drill.

Auntie Jean set off for home on the Sunday afternoon taking with her our good wishes and leaving behind a rather astonished Yorkshire terrier. It was turning cool and I threw some logs on the fire as the little dog sat on the hearthrug looking rather forlorn. Acol didn't go into any histrionics such as dashing around the room yelping piteously. She just sat and looked at the fire, glancing occasionally up at me.

Jinx stalked into the room and before anyone could say knife, they were at it again, neither of them asking or giving quarter. We hurriedly snatched them apart, Jean administering admonishment to both animals in her best schoolmarm manner. Funnily enough, apart from one incident which followed a little later, they never did fight again after that Sunday afternoon, although the relationship between them could at best only be described as an armed truce.

Whatever strains had been put upon Acol by her sudden removal to a new home, her appetite was unaffected as was evidenced by the swift demolition job that she did on the bowl of food which Jean placed on the kitchen floor for her shortly after the skirmish with Jinx. The meal finished at breakneck speed, she belched loudly and went back to the fire. Jinx kept to the other side of the hearthrug and, apart from the odd hiss or low growl, we all settled down to a relatively quiet evening. Auntie Jean had left Acol's basket, which we had placed in a corner of the kitchen, so we didn't contemplate any problems with the sleeping arrangements as Jinx, who usually preferred to spend the night hours out of doors anyway, would be fully occupied with her kittens in the hall.

The cat leapt for Jean's lap as she returned from putting Stephen to bed and I tickled the dog's ears as she sat gazing into the flames.

"Well," I said, gazing thoughtfully at the tousled head and pricked ears, "you're starting another part of your life now, young lady, so I suppose you had better have a new name to go with it."

"What?" inquired Jean, as she curled her legs beneath her on the sofa.

"A new name," I replied.

"You can't give her a new name at her age. She

won't answer to it and anyway Acol is a rather unusual name, and very distinguished too." Jean was probably remembering the bit about the President of Nicaragua.

"It's a bloody silly name for a dog," I said, "and if you think I'm going to be seen out with her in our district shouting 'Acol, Acol' every time she runs off you've got another think coming."

"It's your mates at the pub, isn't it?" grinned Jean facetiously. "You're scared they'll think you're going a bit soft or something. Tell you what, I'll tie a nice little ribbon in her hair and you can take her for walkies tomorrow night while it's still light so that they can all get a good look at you."

"It's not that," I protested (she was quite right of course), "the name 'Acol' lacks... er... well... dignity. Yes that's it, dignity. She's probably a right little terror (how right I was) and 'Acol' is just not right. And the other bit about her not answering to a new name is not valid. It doesn't matter what we call her so long as we call her it often enough, especially at grub time." Jean gave me an old fashioned look and continued with the book she was reading. I gazed into the fire and silence fell, broken only by loud purrs from Jinx as Jean stroked her head. After a few moments Jean looked up from her book.

"What did you have in mind?" she asked.

"Eh?" I answered still looking into the fire.

"The new name for Acol, what did you have in mind?"

14

I sat back in my chair and gazed at the ceiling as if in deep thought.

"Come on," said Jean, "you brought the subject up, so you must have thought of something. What?"

"Fred," I answered shortly.

"What?" howled Jean, incredulously.

"Well, she reminds me of Fred Hathersage," I replied defensively. (Fred Hathersage is one of the local eccentrics. He shaves about every third week and has rather long pointed ears.)

"Don't be insulting."

"Who are we insulting, the dog or Fred?" I said.

"Anyway," continued Jean, "Fred is a preposterous name for a little lady dog."

"How does Frederika strike you then?" I asked.

"Sounds rather like a deposed Royal from some dubious Balkan state," answered Jean. The matter rested there until supper time when I had one of my rare flashes of inspiration. Taking a broken piece of biscuit from the coffee table, I offered it to the dog.

"Here Fred," I called and Acol trotted over to me and greedily gobbled it up. "See?" I said triumphantly. "She answers to Fred."

"She'd answer to Esmerelda Swillbucket if there was a biscuit at the end each time," observed Jean.

We bedded the dog down in the kitchen and went to bed with the matter unresolved. Jean went to sleep almost immediately, having taken a couple of tablets to cure the headache resulting from the hectic weekend, but I lay awake in the darkness thinking about the new addition to the family and wondering whether Auntie Jean was telling the truth when she said that the dog was housetrained.

Next day Steve proved to be an unexpected ally in my battle to change the dog's name. He thought that 'Fred' was a capital name for a dog, so we made a secret pact to say nothing more of the matter but henceforth 'Fred' was the name we would use. Jean kept up the protestations for three or four days but in the end she capitulated in the face of overwhelming opposition from father and son. Fred, it seemed, couldn't care less what people called her as long as she was properly housed, fed and groomed.

Although the cat and dog tolerated each other, I always thought that Jinx had the upper hand but I was to be proved wrong during one feeding time when Fred finally asserted her authority. For convenience we fed the two of them at the same time, although at opposite ends of the kitchen. Jinx liked dog food and indeed would eat little else but she seemed to think the grass was always greener on the other side of the fence, and the other side of the fence on this particular occasion was Fred's bowl of meat. With all the arrogance of a master race, Jinx stalked over to the bowl where Fred was eating. Very delicately she extended a paw into the bowl to scoop up some meat and – wham! I always maintain that it was all over in three seconds but Jean insists it was nearer two. Without uttering a sound, Fred moved with a speed which was beyond belief, seized Jinx by the scruff of the neck, hurled her two yards across the

16

kitchen and, still without making a sound, carried on eating. There was a stunned silence. Only Jinx's pride had been hurt and, as she had landed in the proximity of her own bowl, she must have decided that discretion was the better part of valour and, with an air of injured innocence, resumed eating from her own bowl. There was no follow up and no more fights.

The grooming was a bit of a problem at first as, while Fred enjoyed eating, lying by the fire and galloping round the garden, she had a marked objection to anything involving a brush or a comb. It took two of us to make any sort of job of it, Jean brushing and combing while I held Fred's head. Steve thought the process highly amusing and chortled happily while Jinx usually sat on the windowsill sneering. Fred never actually bit me during these performances but she went in for a lot of growling and struggling. Nowadays she reluctantly submits but is still not over keen and, if she sees Jean with a brush in her hand, she goes into hiding.

After a few days we decided to give her a bath and the results were even more alarming.

'Reassure your pet and it will stand quietly in the sink, enjoying the luxurious sensation of the cleansing and invigorating lather of Maxo Medicated Dog Shampoo.'

At least that was what it said on the bottle. The trouble was that Fred couldn't read.

"Hold her head," screamed Jean, up to her armpits in lather as the suds flew all over the kitchen.

"I can't find her bloody head in this lot," I howled. I groped under the suds and found something solid.

"That's my hand, Twit!" I groped around again. Fred shoved her head up through the foam and spattered the kitchen walls with large blobs of suds as she shook her head violently.

"You've put too much stuff in," Jean yelled, as I grabbed Fred's head while I had the chance.

"No I haven't," I replied as Jean struggled on, "it says a cupful on the label."

Jean glanced at the bottle on the worktop by the sink.

"It says A CAPFUL – you idiot," she roared. "Strewth," she grinned, "no wonder it looks like a Chinese Laundry in here. Still," she added, "at least she'll be clean."

The foam flowed over onto the kitchen floor, much to Stephen's delight, and we began to rinse Fred in warm clean water. At least Jean did. I was too busy fighting a losing battle with the white bubbles that threatened to engulf the kitchen.

Eventually we got the mess cleaned up and Fred thoroughly dried out with a rough towel. The grooming began shortly afterwards and when we had finished I had to admit that Fred really did look a rather handsome little lady. She was handsome alright but, as time went by, we were to find out that whatever Fred was, she was certainly no lady.

3

Getting to Know the 'Locals'

Around the time Fred came to live with us Jean was in the process of returning to a teaching career. Stephen was attending nursery school in preparation for his full time start at the local church primary school a few months later. So Jean had started teaching, on a part-time basis, at a nearby infants' school, getting back into the swing of things, as she put it.

Although prior to Stephen's arrival the bulk of her teaching had been done at secondary level, Jean felt that she would like to have a crack at teaching mathematics and other subjects (except geography, of course) to the seven to eleven age group. That is what she eventually did although, to hear her when she arrives home from her present school sometimes, anyone overhearing the conversation might be excused for forming the impression that she had spent the day with thirty hell bent miniature assassins on an army commando assault course.

The reason for my mentioning this is that the school

teaching had an indirect bearing on the matter of exercising the dog.

It had been agreed, at the time when Jean had been flinging about the wild promises in her battle to convince me of the absolute necessity of giving Fred a home, that any dog walking would naturally fall to her. At that time Jean was prepared to walk Fred each evening, come whatever the weather, and to thoroughly brush and groom our new pet every day.

However, in the event of the dog's arrival and permanent establishment in the household, the desire on Jean's part to dash out of the house at six o'clock sharp each evening for the walking exercise diminished in direct proportion to the length of time since Fred's arrival.

One evening Jean arrived home from school in a state of near total exhaustion (at least that was the impression she intended to create), threw herself on the sofa before the fire and proceeded to inform anyone who was prepared to listen that "the legs had gone". Steve began to count legs, got to two and gave me a puzzled look.

"It's the kids," Jean moaned in a low voice, "they're running me ragged. I can't keep pace with them, and look – look here… " She lifted her skirt and, turning slightly, pointed to a small blue line behind her knee.

"A varicose vein – my first one – suddenly I feel old," she wailed. Steve and I giggled. Jean was twenty-nine.

"Unfeeling brutes," she glowered, lowering the hem of her skirt and, eyes closed, she kicked off her shoes and wriggled her toes before the blazing fire.

"What's Mum on about?" asked Steve in the sort of whisper that could be heard in the next room. Jean opened one eye and gave us a baleful look. Fred came in to join our group, sitting by my feet, while Jinx sat on the arm of the sofa and gave our trio a dirty look. There was no doubt whose side Jinx was on, just as there was no doubt as to who would be walking the dog that night.

Jean just managed to make it unassisted to the table and, after demolishing a bowl of soup, a huge plateful of beef casserole and a generous portion of apple pie with cream, she staggered back to the sofa clutching a large cup of tea which, despite the staggering, she skilfully avoided spilling.

"It doesn't affect your appetite then, this school thing," I observed, "just the legs is it?"

"Yeh," replied Jean, "just the legs."

Steve shot up to his bedroom to play and I joined my wife by the fire.

"Supposing… just supposing," I began, "that I volunteered to walk Fred tonight… "

"I would do the washing up," finished Jean and, leaping to her feet, she began to clear the table.

"You are good really," she said. "It's awfully lonely walking her in the dark. Anyway if I know you, I've got a pretty good idea where Fred will be going tonight and you've never complained about previous visits."

"How're the legs now?" I inquired.

"I suppose," replied Jean from the kitchen, "it's what you might call a miracle cure."

I looked down at Fred. "Come on, my little pal, I'm

going to give you your dinner and then you and I are going visiting."

Fred finished off her bowl of meat and meal and began to lap at the clean water that I had put down for her.

"Don't drink too much, dear," said Jean sweetly, glancing in Fred's direction, "or you won't have room for anymore when you get where you are going."

"Any bloody sarcasm," I began, "and I'll have a sudden attack of gout or something."

"Sorry... sorry," grinned Jean, holding up one hand, "no offence intended."

An hour later, Fred was on her lead scrambling at the back kitchen door and, with a fond farewell from my newly healed wife and instructions to 'make sure she does her things', we set off into the night.

Jean always refers to the various bodily functions as 'things' or 'bits and pieces'. We had a hilarious period when Stephen was small and just learning to use his potty without giving everybody a bit of each. An American child psychologist insisted in his book that the act of defecation should be referred to as B.M. (bowel movement). Upon Jean's insistence Stephen was taught to use the expression, much to her delight. The only trouble was that nobody else, including the immediate family, understood what the hell he was talking about so he doesn't use it any more.

Fred turned right as we went out on to the lane but I gently corrected her and we set off in the other direction.

"That's the way to the Chequers," I explained, "we are going to the Nags Head first. We'll call at the Chequers later."

The little dog understood perfectly and I began to have high hopes of her as we trotted off up the lane. I subsequently found out from Auntie Jean that she had had a lot of trouble keeping Fred out of the local Conservative Club in Yorkshire, so the speed with which Fred assessed the area's pub situation was perhaps not surprising.

Right on cue, Fred, pulling at the lead, took the correct turn off the lane and into the back yard of the Nags and any feelings of guilt that may have remained in my mind were quickly dispelled as, straining and tugging even harder, she made a beeline for the back door.

I think that was when Fred and I really fell in love.

4

Weightlifter!

No super star at the London Palladium could ever have made a greater hit with the fans than a Yorkshire terrier made with the customers at the Nags Head that night. It wasn't just the pub, it certainly wasn't the beer (Fred doesn't drink alcohol), it was the people. I found out then that Fred adores people – especially in pubs, where they are likely to supply a small appealing dog with a never ending stream of nuts, crisps, ham rolls, more nuts and then a clean ashtray full of clear water to wash the salt out of her mouth before she bids them goodnight. In return she offers companionship, tail wagging and occasionally, but only if forced, the rare sit up and beg.

I thought that after the Nags Head, the visit to the Chequers would prove something of an anticlimax but, as is generally the case, I was wrong. It was in the Chequers Hotel that Fred really stamped her presence and authority on the local community.

To realise just how she achieved this it is necessary to understand the nature of the pastimes pursued by certain members of our community. Some of these activities, whilst not what one would really call criminal, are not strictly within the letter of the law as laid down in the statute books. While secretly or tacitly approved by an embarrassingly large proportion of naturally law-abiding residents, these activities are a source of constant irritation, interspersed with occasional outbursts of violent anger, to farmers, landowners and the county constabulary.

Not to put too fine a point on it, the place is full of poachers. These people are held in high esteem by all, except by farmers, landowners and the county constabulary, partly because of the nerve and skill required in the illegal pursuit of game, and partly because of the rabbits, hares and other things that get thrown around like confetti when the lads have had a good day or night.

The local bobbies don't mind too much if the poaching isn't done on their patch and the fact that game stew is eaten by some policemen's families in the area is pure coincidence.

Should one of these splendid fellows actually mention that you need a haircut, the last place to go is the local barber's shop. Far better to follow him out of the pub where the chances are you may be permitted to purchase a four legged, long eared variety of 'hair' for a nominal sum. Spelling is not a strong point among poachers, but this is not important as everybody seems to understand each other perfectly well.

Various methods are employed for this illicit taking

of game but, with regard to hare and rabbits, the use of dogs is particularly favoured. It is strongly rumoured that one local farmer has been known to throw apoplectic fits at the sight of one of my friends walking his Jack Russell terrier and pair of whippets down the street. I cannot understand why this farmer should be so overcome with anger at such an innocent pastime as dog walking and, if you believe that, you'll believe anything.

The reason that dogs are so favoured has nothing to do with the thrill of the chase as, I am told, is experienced in fox hunting. Funnily enough most poachers are violently opposed to fox hunting, regarding it on the whole as rather cruel. Snares are frowned upon as causing unnecessary suffering and shotguns either leave too many pellets in the flesh of the animal being killed or do not kill but maim, leaving the victim to struggle away to die in agony. A trained whippet kills quickly and cleanly and with a minimum of fuss. I once drew the parallel between foxhounds and whippets in conversation with a poaching friend of mine but, as he remarked to me that next time I might like to try stewed fox, I took his point and we switched the conversation to football.

Nobody worth his salt uses shotguns anyway these days as the results are rather messy and a far more professional job, when poaching game birds, can be accomplished with a high powered .22 air rifle, telescopic sight and torch. Anyway shotguns make too much noise and are best left to people who like to kill birds for fun. Or so I am reliably informed.

So you can see that dogs have a role in local society and it is important that they should command respect in their particular field.

The bar of the Chequers was fairly quiet that night, but in the corner near the bar the usual collection of 'regulars' greeted me with the grunt and nod that is the signal of acceptance and friendship in our part of the world. Fred trotted behind me and it was a moment or two before anyone noticed her. Ears pricked and stubby tail twitching, there was nothing nervous about her as she eyed the two whippets quietly snoozing the evening away at the feet of one of my friends.

"And just what the hell is that?" inquired Ray, easing his eighteen stone sideways on his stool and nodding in Fred's direction.

"It's an elephant," I answered, taking a pull at a pint of Bass. "Haven't you ever seen an elephant before?"

"It's a Yorkie," said Dave peering over the table. (A very bright lad is Dave), "I've heard about them. Cheeky little buggers some of 'em."

"It's only got one eye," observed Stuart.

One of Brian's whippets opened an eye and glanced at Fred, then shuffled herself into a more comfortable position and dropped off to sleep again. Fred sat down on the floor by my stool.

Suddenly Ray stamped his foot and grinned fiercely at Fred. She didn't flinch but looked up at him steadily with her one good eye.

"Well," he observed, "it ain't frightened easily."

"I reckon," said Dave, "if you keep doing that,

Raymond, you might regret it. I've heard about them, they think they're miniature lions."

"What's his name?" asked Stuart, "Nelson?"

"It's not a he, it's a she, and she's called Fred."

Nobody seemed surprised at the name. Ray peered down at her through the veil of smoke coming from the cigarette held loosely in his fingers. Fred stared back.

"Grrrr… " said Ray, pulling a face. He picked up his pint, drained the glass, set it back on the bar and, calling for a round of drinks, dropped the stub of his cigarette on the floor and ground it out with the sole of his shoe.

And that was Ray's big mistake.

Fred, it seemed, had had just about a gutful of people stamping feet at her for one night and, in a blur of black and tan, she leapt forward and nipped Ray smartly on the instep.

I have never believed in levitation, and how a nine pound dog can lift eighteen stone two feet vertically in half a second is a mystery to me. But we all saw it happen, for suddenly Ray was standing on his stool.

After maybe two seconds of total silence, laughter roared around the bar. To his everlasting credit nobody laughed louder than Ray as he gingerly climbed down from his rocking perch.

And then a strange thing happened. Fred went up to him, jumped up and began to lick his hand.

"Hey," he grinned broadly, "she's saying 'sorry', she likes me after all."

"Yeah," said Stuart, "provided you don't stamp your foot at her, eh Dave?… Dave?"

Dave had disappeared behind the table. We all peered over to inspect him and saw that he had assumed the foetal position while his body slowly shook in sobbing tremors. Ray tapped him on the shoulder. "Dave… eh… Dave?"

"His face is going purple," said Brian. "Do you think he's having a fit or something?"

Slowly uncurling himself with tears streaming down his face, Dave looked at Fred and, mouth opening and closing silently, promptly disappeared behind the table again, only this time the laughter was audible as manic giggling.

"It wasn't that funny," said Ray, now stroking Fred's head.

"It was from over here," Dave managed to burst out between the sobs which racked his body. Pulling himself upright again he looked down at the little dog. "If you can do that again, my old pal, I'll give you twenty quid. I've been waiting for years for something like that to happen to that bugger."

"Won't happen again," said Ray, stroking Fred's ears as she lay in his lap. "We're mates now, aren't we?" Fred licked his hand affectionately. It seemed that they understood one another.

And that was it. Fred was totally accepted into the community as an upright member of society who commanded respect from all. Throughout the whole performance the whippets never stirred but then perhaps they were relaxing after a hard day's work in the field. At least I assume so, because when we left the Chequers I held Fred in my left hand while a rabbit, held firmly by the ears, swung from my right.

Now you can understand why Jean does not altogether trust me about her friend's rabbits.

Steve and I love rabbit pie.

5

Killer Instinct

Sunday is the one day of the week that, as a family, we tend to keep very much for ourselves. As I spend most Saturdays working it is the only time when we can be together all day and, although Steve is growing older and tends to wander off for ever lengthening periods, we rather enjoy each other's company.

Jean does not display any great bursts of energy on Sunday mornings or on any other mornings for that matter. It is usually Steve and I who are up and about around half past eight leaving a bump in the bedclothes that can be coaxed downstairs by the smell of frying bacon, sometime after nine o'clock.

I suppose that Steve and I are, what are nowadays fashionably called 'morning persons', while Jean, who will watch television into the small hours, is definitely a 'night person'. Left alone for an hour or so after rising, she normally resumes her cheerful personality but any shocks or sudden loud noises before the second cup of tea after breakfast can trigger off some surprising and occasionally alarming consequences.

On one beautiful sunny Sunday morning in the late spring of the year following Fred's arrival Steve, probably awakened early by the sunshine pouring in through his bedroom window, quietly but insistently dragged me out of bed sometime before eight o'clock. It was one of those magic mornings that luckier adults can remember from childhood. A light white mist hung in the still air but the sky above was blue and the soft sunlight made the dew sparkle. Steve opened the kitchen door and Fred rocketed out on to the lawn, tumbling over and over in the wet grass uttering small growling noises of delight before doing a few quick laps of the garden as an encore.

It was a little early for breakfast so I made a cup of tea while Steve tucked into his 'first course' of cornflakes. He insisted on pouring his own milk as he was now a fully paid up member of St. John's Primary School and he considered himself very grown up.

Just how grown up for a five-year-old we were both shortly to find out.

I saw Edie through the kitchen window walking down the lane towards our back door. Edie (she hates her name Edith) is one of our oldest friends and lives only a few doors away from us. It was not unusual to see her out and about early as she seems to be one of these people of limitless energy and is a renowned early riser. She is also one of the most cheerful people I know and is almost always smiling, but there was no smile on her face that morning. Edie was crying and she was heading straight for our back garden. I put down my mug of tea, quietly opened the door and, stepping out onto the path, walked slowly towards her.

"What's the matter, Edie?" I asked softly, putting my arm around her shoulders. Edie gazed up at me, eyes swimming.

"There's a cat lying in the gutter up the lane. It's been run over and it looks very much like... ... ... "

"Jinx?" I finished.

"She's not here is she?"

It was more a statement of fact than a question and the truth was that I hadn't seen Jinx around that morning. Usually she would be hanging around somewhere, either sitting on the fence or climbing one of the cherry trees in the front garden when she returned from her nocturnal activities.

"Well, we'd better go and find out, love," I said.

"What's the matter, Dad?" called Steve.

"Hang on a minute, Edie," I said, "I'd forgotten about Steve."

He was finishing the last of his cornflakes as I walked into the room.

"Dad?"

"Look, mate," I began, "I want you to do me a big favour. Stay here for a minute, I shan't be long and whatever you do keep quiet and don't wake Mum up. O.K?"

Steve looked at me steadily, perhaps too steadily for a five-year-old, I thought later.

"O.K. Dad," he replied, "I'll play with my Lego 'til you cook the bacon."

Edie and I trailed up the lane followed by Fred, who sensed that something was afoot and was determined not to be left out.

The three of us stood and looked at the black twisted heap at the side of the lane. It was Jinx alright; her small mouth open and a pool of blood already coagulating around the smashed head and broken back.

Edie looked down at the small black bundle "It's them bloody cars you know," she said tearfully. I nodded. It certainly wasn't low flying aircraft, I thought. She began to cry again, Fred whimpered and I didn't exactly feel a bundle of fun either.

"Go home now, Edie," I said, "and thanks for telling me."

"S'alright, but what are you going to say to Jean?" she asked.

"I'll think about that in a while," I replied. "She'll no doubt be round to see you soon anyway."

"Yes," She looked at Jinx again. "Yes – send her round." She paused and wiped her eyes, "I'll go and get the kids' breakfast."

With Fred trotting at my heels I carried Jinx home. Fred hopped in the kitchen door and, as I placed the little body on the grass, I saw Steve watching me through the window. I went into the house and my small son looked up at me with damp eyes.

"She got run over didn't she, Dad?" he said quietly.

"Yes my old pal, I'm afraid so." He brushed away a tear and sniffed loudly.

"Dad… I've not woken Mum up… or anything," he finished lamely.

I felt very proud of Steve.

A light mist fell across my eyes as I hung the spade back on the hook on the garage wall after I had buried Jinx in a deep grave in the garden beside the fence. Momentarily annoyed with myself, I brushed the tears away, went back into the house and made a fresh cup of tea. Steve was quietly stroking Fred as she lay on the hearth rug.

Cup and saucer in hand, I made my way upstairs. This was going to be the worst part.

"'Ello." Jean blinked sleepily at me and then, as she caught the look in my eyes, alarm flooded across her face.

"It's bad news, love," I said clumsily, "Jinx has been run over."

I waited for the tears and cries of anguish but I could see that what I had said had not quite sunk in.

"What?" she said quietly.

I told her again. Then the anguish and tears came in a great flood as she started to get out of bed. Slowly, but firmly, I pushed her back.

"Where is she? I must see her."

"It's too late," I said, "I've buried her."

"Where?"

"In the garden by the fence. It's best you didn't see her. It was a car I think. She must have been killed outright."

I had sudden crazy thoughts about low flying aircraft which just shows what lunatic tricks the mind plays at times.

Stephen stood forlornly at the bedroom door. Leaving Jean to get up slowly, he and I went downstairs. Fred sat watching us, sensing the feeling of doom spreading over the house. Then she looked at Steve and her tail twitched ever so slightly, her ears pricked, Jinxie was gone but Fred was still there.

I grinned at Steve. "She could do with a walk."

"Come on, Fred." he said, racing to the kitchen for her lead. I watched them run up the garden path, Fred pulling for all she was worth.

The mist cleared away and the sun grew hotter, shining from a clear blue sky.

* * *

Jean called a national week of mourning. The way things were going, after two days, half the village was convinced that somebody had shot the Queen and all the newspapers and T.V. had missed the event.

Everybody who would listen was given a blow by blow account of the happenings of that Sunday morning, with particular stress on the bravery and fortitude displayed by the lady of the house, with a small mention of the supporting roles of husband and son. But gradually the hurt passed and Jean embarked on a programme of rehabilitation which consisted of adopting kittens.

We had two.

The first one took a look at Fred and decided that, despite the attention lavished upon her, the house was not for her. She kept running away, each time pursued by Jean and a posse of recruited neighbours. Steve and I were of the opinion that it was no good trying to replace Jinx, but try telling that to a cat-loving woman with the bit firmly between her teeth.

Eventually the kitten/cat made it to the Lord alone knows where, only to be replaced a few days later by another one. This one lasted a little while longer until a neighbour was reversing his Volkswagen.

"They were trying to get away," wailed Jean, "Why?… Why?… I love them and care for them and feed them and… " Fred yawned, stretched on the rug, thumped her tail a couple of times and, giving a great sigh, sank into what I can only assume to be the doggie equivalent of untroubled sleep.

We don't have a cat now.

* * *

What followed put us all in an extremely embarrassing position. The situation in which we found ourselves was aggravated because the whole event was clouded in uncertainty.

Edie's cat, Smoky, disappeared.

Smoky was a Persian type. I say type because all the cats in our area seem to be of a 'type' and not a 'breed'. Maybe this has something to do with an exaggerated sexuality among local moggies and a marked lack of supervision by their owners.

"He's been gone two weeks now," said Edie over a cup of tea with Jean. "He's gone before but never for this long."

Jean sympathised, having had no little experience in chasing cats.

It was about that time that an incident occurred which, to me, seemed totally unrelated to the disappearance of Smoky who, incidentally, never returned. I was at home alone. Jean had gone off with Steve to visit one of her sisters. Fred had taken to wandering about the immediate neighbourhood in search of rats, real and imaginary. One day she actually brought one home, stone dead, with a neat bite at the back of the neck and proudly deposited it outside the back door; much to Jean's disgust and to cries of admiration from Steve and myself.

This particular day she trotted down the path looking distinctly battered. Fresh blood flecked her nose and pieces of her coat seemed to be missing, although it's always difficult to tell with Fred as, unless she has been freshly bathed and combed, she is one of the scruffiest tykes around. I sponged her muzzle and found a couple of scratches but, after she had demolished a bowl of food, she was none the worse and, true to form, dropped off to sleep in front of the fire.

The incident hardly seemed worth mentioning, although I did say to Jean that I thought she had been ratting that afternoon and had bitten off a bit more than she could chew.

The search for Smoky dwindled and died and then

one night, a few weeks later, as Fred and I were returning from the Nags Head, I fell into casual conversation with an acquaintance who lives higher up the lane and is a keen vegetable gardener.

"That's yourn, is it then?" he said quietly, looking at Fred.

"Aye," I said, "that's Fred."

"Ow's not very big, but ow did a bloody good job on that Persian wot's been digging up my peas."

"What Persian?" I asked anxiously.

"Brok its bloody neck, clean as yer like. Good dog that." Fred wagged her tail. "'Ave yer put yer beans in yet? I put mine in yesterday, but it's a bit early... frost yer know."

"Yeh," I said. "What about the Persian?" I said.

"Bloody good dog that... clean as a whistle... G'night, Rog." He tramped back up his garden path. I looked down at Fred as we walked down the lane.

"You've dropped us right in it this time, mate," I said.

"What shall we do?" asked Jean, when I got home and told her what had happened.

"Not a lot," I said. "What can we do? There are lots of Persian types around... and lots of Yorkshire terriers."

"Don't be silly." Jean's vocabulary can be very limited at times, particularly when she is under stress.

"I think we'll keep our mouths shut," I said.

"There isn't much more we can do, is there?" she said. "But I don't know how I'm going to face Edie."

"Pretend it didn't happen?" I said hopefully.

"Don't be silly," said Jean.

39

6

To 'Er' is Human

"I know somebody who has a dog," Jean announced proudly one day. Not original I thought but, before I could make a suitable comment, Stephen rushed in with the observation that his pal Mark had a dog.

"It's sort of brown and white and its tail sticks up and it's got floppy ears and… … … "

"I mean," said Jean heavily, "a Yorkshire terrier dog."

Stephen subsided and looked blankly at me. Then we both looked at Jean expectantly.

"We are now going to be let in to one of the great secrets of the universe, Steve," I said.

"Oh," said Steve. We sat in silence.

"Now then," said Jean, "according to my calculation, anytime now Fred should be ready and we would be foolish not to, considering Nicaragua and so forth."

"It's a geography lesson," I said brightly.

"No it's not, and don't be so stupid." Jean said. "I mean that Fred will be… well… ready… you know and, with these people having a dog, I think it would be a good idea to let her mate and have some more puppies."

"I don't like it," said Steve.

"What?"

"Geography, we had it in school today. It's all about countries and far off lands."

He looked at me. "What's it got to do with Yorkshire terriers, Dad?"

"Geography is all about foreign places like Yorkshire." I said.

"Is Yorkshire a foreign country, Mum?" asked Steve.

"No it is not," howled Jean, danger signals flashing in her eyes. "Well," she said, "what do you think?"

Now in our house you are allowed to think all you like provided you don't talk about it too much. So I sat and thought. "I don't know much about it really," I said. Quick as a knife thrust, Jean was in.

"You knew enough about it when we had him," she said, nodding at Steve.

"Ah yes," I recovered, "but he's not a dog, are you, Steve?"

"Don't think so, Dad," he said.

The woman who had the dog was a friend of a friend and was willing to mate it with Fred for the 'pick of the litter'. Jean and I had only the foggiest of ideas about dog breeding. As we found out later, the last thing to do is to give anyone the pick of the litter.

Jean fixed a time and a date and then went down with 'flu, so it was 'Jimmy Muggins' who set out with Fred one evening for the attempt. It was a modern house on a new housing development and we were greeted at the front door by a young and rather pretty lady, clutching a Yorkie to her rather overdeveloped bosom.

"He's called Pepe... You must be Mr... er... yes well... come in and bring... er... your... er... with you."

I sat down on the smart settee and looked at the smart carpet and smart television set and wondered how on earth I had been conned by Jean into this situation in the first place. During the drive down I had been comforted by the thought that, while I didn't have the slightest idea what I was doing, the lady with the dog would be experienced in these matters and, as Fred had already produced three litters, the whole business would be second nature to her.

I was a fool.

After five minutes it was obvious that the lady was regretting every minute of the time she had spent setting up the project and, like me, didn't know what the hell to do.

"Er... Mr... er... I think we ought to put them in the... er... kitchen," she smiled nervously. "Er... to get to know one another you know."

"Er... yes, O.K." I said.

"Bloody hell," I thought, "She's got me at it now."

So I took them into the kitchen, quietly told Fred to get on with it and closed the door.

"We'll leave them for a while and perhaps they will er... you know... er," she said.

We sat in silence, staring at the wall. The first indication of any activity was a spate of snarling and growling and, as I opened the kitchen door hoping to see the pair proceeding with the business in hand, I couldn't help but notice that Fred had Pepe by the hind leg and was doing her utmost to throw him out of the window, whirling him round and round as his screams grew louder.

"Er... he's a bit aggressive, er... Mr... er," came a voice from the sitting room.

"Not half as aggressive as Fred," I thought. I kicked her smartly up the backside and she let go of Pepe's leg. The dog shot into the other room and Fred suddenly developed a marked interest in the kitchen waste bin which had been overturned in the fight.

They say it is a wise man who knows when to call 'Enough'. I make no pretence to wisdom but that night Solomon would have finished a poor second. Grabbing Fred, I staggered into the room where Mrs... Er was comforting a distraught Pepe.

"Perhaps she's not quite ready," I said (oh yes, I'd read the relevant books and much good it had done me). "Maybe we could try later, in a day or two."

"Liar." I thought as I said it. I had no intention of ever going near the place again.

"Er... yes... er... " she said, stroking Pepe. "I think there's something wrong with Pepe's leg."

"Probably cramp." I said. "Anyway, we'll be getting along."

"Er... yes"

"Be in touch."

"Er... yes," she said, as she escorted me to the door

43

clutching a terrified Pepe. "Sorry it wasn't… er… " she said as I went down the path, Fred sitting in the crook of my arm and glaring at Pepe.

"Yes," I said, "never mind."

"Goodbye, Mr… er… "

"Goodbye," I said. I opened the door of the car and Fred walloped on to the back seat and promptly went to sleep. I looked for the nearest pub and, after a quick pint to calm my nerves, drove slowly home.

"How did it go?" asked Jean brightly, now totally recovered from the 'flu.

"It didn't," I said, "unless you count fighting and general household disruption."

"She didn't… er… " said Jean.

"If you say 'er', I'll pick you up, put you across my knee and spank you 'til you can't sit down." I said.

"Why?" she asked.

So I told her.

After Jean had stopped giggling, she became more serious and said, "I would so like her to have some more puppies."

I agreed it was a problem but, as it turned out, it was a problem which Fred solved for us, in a not totally satisfactory way.

The Great Escape

A few days later Steve and I had a most interesting lecture on doors. Jean impressed upon us both how important doors were and what a large part they played in our lives. Doors, apparently, were for opening to get into places but, more importantly, they were for closing to keep out things like draughts and to keep in things like small Yorkshire terrier bitches that were in heat. Of course I understood the position perfectly and Steve struggled manfully to keep a look of intelligent comprehension on his face.

"So you see," finished Jean, "it is important to close doors at all times… particularly now."

We both nodded seriously. Then Steve asked, "Why have we got to be careful now?"

I grinned and looked at Jean, "Come on, love, you're the teacher."

"Well," she said carefully, then launched into a highly adapted version of 'the birds and the bees'. When she had finished she beamed at Stephen and said, "So there you are… see?"

"Yes, Mum," persisted our son, "but *how* do they do it?"

"Never mind," said Jean briskly, "they do, so now we're all going to be careful aren't we?"

"Yes we are," we chorused dutifully and then Stephen went out to play and promptly left the back door open. A great deal of colourful language followed and Stephen learned two new words.

The following day we were visited by Kerry, a handsome Cairn terrier who lived at the shop just down the road. He worked a shift system, arriving promptly at nine o'clock in the morning and sitting patiently outside the back door until twelve noon when he went home for lunch. Half past one saw him back again until his day ended at four o'clock when he went home for tea. He was never a nuisance and was always very friendly to all – except other dogs. But it was obvious that a very basic and natural instinct occupied most of his thoughts as he kept his sentry go.

The trouble was you just couldn't 'shoo' Kerry away. We tried two or three times and he would assume an expression of wounded pride and sedately trot off, only to return in half an hour or so. At least he kept the garden clear of the other local Romeos when he was on duty. A perfect gentleman was our Kerry.

After a lot of heart-searching we had decided not to mate Fred in her current season. Jean remarked that we had found out just how little we knew and, even after phone calls to Auntie Jean to make enquiries, we were still very much in the dark.

"I reckon we ought to get to know a reputable breeder," said Jean, "and leave it 'til Fred's next season."

"Good idea," I said, sighing with relief, "but what are we going to do about her now?" I pointed at Fred.

"Get a spray," said Jean. "Those aerosol things. You spray the bitch's whotsit and it keeps all the dogs off."

So we sprayed Fred and it was about as much use as a chocolate teapot. If anything it made matters worse.

"I reckon we've been done," I said. "That stuff works more as a 'come on' than a 'put off'."

And then it happened. Somebody left the door open and the sex symbol of Church Street was away. There has been argument to this day as to who left the door open… I reckon it was Jean. Jean says it must have been Steve and he vacillates between Jean and me.

She was gone for two hours. Jean mustered a search party. Of course Edie was roped in and we searched the neighbourhood for half an hour, all to no avail. Jean could be heard muttering softly to herself and at one point Stephen inquired of me what was meant by 'Scarlet Woman'. After half an hour we got fed up and went home for a cup of tea.

"Whatever is going to happen must have happened by now." I said.

"That doesn't sound quite right," said Jean, "but I know what you mean."

An hour passed, Jean's agitation mounting with each minute.

"I ought to have gone with her," said Steve, "then I could have seen how they… "

"Shut up!" yelled Jean.

We all fell silent.

"She might have just gone for a walk," said Jean hopefully.

"Yeh," I said and, pointing out of the window, informed her that there were three pigs flying backwards over the house across the road.

Another half hour passed during which time Jean fretted and fumed and then, glancing out of the kitchen window, she let out a howl which had us racing for the back door.

"She's back!"

With a stupid grin plastered over her face, Fred came down the path followed in convoy by a Jack Russell, a collie, a small mongrel and, of all things, an Alsatian. I would have liked to say that she walked home, but staggered was a fairer description. Her back legs barely functioned. She looked up at Jean and twitched her tail a couple of times.

"Whore!" screamed Jean. Fred wagged her tail again.

"What's a… " began Stephen before I clamped a hand firmly over his mouth.

Beside herself with fury mixed with relief that Fred was back, Jean scooped her up in her arms, threw her in the sink and turned on the cold water tap.

"There, that'll cool your ardour, you little… little. Oh!"

"Fat lot of good that's going to do," I said. "Talk about shutting the gate after the horse has gone."

"Well she deserves it," said Jean, but the anger had

dissipated in floods of relief that Fred was home safe, if not altogether sound.

Fred was towelled dry and all at once, with that lightning switch of emotions peculiar to women, Jean suddenly became solicitous as to her well-being, making cooing noises and inquiring, "Are we going to have some puppies then?"

"We'd make a fortune if we all had puppies," I observed as Steve and I went out to kick a football around. Of course we closed the back door behind us and as I looked up the lane I saw Kerry trotting past our garden on his way home.

For the first time in my life I'll swear a dog winked at me.

* * *

That summer proved to be every child's delight and every gardener's despair. From late May until early September each day dawned, seemingly more golden than the last; while the grass lost its green sheen to grow steadily browner under the constant glare. Hosepipes were surreptitiously deployed late at night in an effort to give the parched gardens hope of life and, I must confess that, after hosepipes and sprinklers were banned by local authorities, I began to despair of my own garden. Fortunately, like most people, I have a little of the Jeckyll and Hyde in me and while Dr Jeckyll was a most law-abiding citizen, I must confess that Mr Hyde was not.

So the cabbage, beans and carrots struggled on and so did Fred. Now severely pregnant, after first of all being slightly and then moderately pregnant, she was finding the hot weather rough going. Looking like a miniature barrel with a leg at each corner, she found solace from the heat in a way which was acceptable to both of us.

The floor of the public bar of the Nags Head is tiled, and in the early evenings Fred and I dutifully made our pilgrimage to carry out cooling operations. I had a quiet pint of bitter and Fred sank down gratefully on to the cool tiles with a sigh of relief which brought a great deal of pleasure to her, and only a little less to the customers of the Inn who took their own in seeing a small dog enjoying herself as much as they were, if in a slightly different way.

All the 'regulars' became most solicitous as to Fred's well-being, and there was much speculation as to the number and type of offspring which she would eventually bear. This speculation was accompanied by much prodding and stroking of Fred's abdomen to which she took no exception, as each prod and stroke was invariably accompanied by an offered crisp or other delicacy which was never refused. Indeed Fred took to the whole procedure quite eagerly, rolling on her back, mouth open expectantly whenever she was approached.

It was two weeks before I found out that some crafty sod was running a book on how many pups she would have and what the cross would be. Most, and indeed all, had heard the story of her sexual exploits and the types of the four dogs which had followed her home on that fateful day. However, I felt that I knew a little more about the event than they did and I knew where my money was going so I kept my mouth tightly shut.

And then, one night, Fred disgraced us both. At least I thought she had disgraced us both, but it turned out that I was the one that bore the disgrace. It was another salutary lesson to me never to try to understand a woman, canine or human. In short, Fred decided that she could wait no longer and deposited a pile in the middle of the floor. Then she gave a low 'woof' to attract my attention and wagged her tail.

I had, at the time, been in deep and serious discussion with a fellow cricket fan as to the wisdom of the inclusion of a certain fast bowler in the England cricket team, shortly to be engaged in the Second Test match of the series. Fred's 'woof' took me from the white on green of the cricket field to the brown on the stone of the floor of the public bar of the Nags Head. Flushed with embarrassment I turned to Iris, the landlady, and, before I could ask for a copy of the Sun to clean up, she handed me a sheaf of paper napkins, nodding understandingly all the time. I removed the offending pile and John, Iris's son, finished off the job with mop and disinfectant, much to the good natured amusement of all concerned, except me.

"Mucky little bugger," I muttered under my breath.

"No she isn't," said Iris, "she's pregnant."

Two ladies at the bar solemnly nodded. "It takes us that way sometimes. You men don't understand," said one.

"Unfeeling sod," said the other as she gave Fred a

crisp and patted her head with a couple of 'there, there's and a 'never mind'.

I had wild visions of the two ladies and the floor of the Nags Head.

The next night I caught the full blast of female unity which only reinforced an already strong belief about women and how they all stick together. Not wishing Fred to repeat the performance of the previous evening, I nevertheless determined to have a pint after playing my Mr Hyde in the garden; so I looped Fred's lead around a drainpipe in the back yard of the Nags and with strict instructions to 'stay', she could do very little else, I went into the bar to be confronted by Iris. Normally, Iris never asks what I want, just pulls me a pint of bitter, but tonight was different.

"Where is she?"

"Outside... er... I didn't want it to happen again and it's very good of you to overlook her indiscretion and... "

"You cruel bugger," said Iris. "You're inhuman. I'll tell you something, if you don't bring that little soul in here you get no drink from this pub. How could you leave her?"

"Tied up to a drainpipe," I finished.

"What?" she yelled.

I hurriedly disappeared into the yard, shortly to return with Fred. "And think yourself lucky you're getting this," said Iris as she placed a pint of bitter on the bar. "I've a good mind to charge you double." I quietly subsided into a corner while Fred went on her rounds before sinking onto the cool tiles.

"Poor little sod," said Iris glaring at me. The ladies nodded. "They don't understand."

"No, they're only men you know." They all glared at me.

I felt alone again.

* * *

While most of my evenings were occupied with work in the garden and walking Fred to and from the Nags and the Chequers, Jean had been raiding the local libraries and had surrounded herself with a stack of books on puppies, concerning their care and how they arrive. I had a good idea about the last bit but Jean told me not to be vulgar. Neither of us knew a great deal and we were even more perplexed by the way many of the books contradicted each other. A great many lengthy telephone calls, on that and other subjects, to Auntie Jean culminated in her spending a long weekend with us.

I get on very well with Auntie Jean and we all had a most enjoyable time, mostly talking about pregnant dogs, birth and the care of puppies. Only one incident slightly unnerved me. The two of them had taken to ringing anybody and everybody getting advice about what to do on the great day and I began to feel increasingly apprehensive as to the size of the telephone bill. I had visions of the envelope landing on the hall floor with a thud which would do very little for an already strained relationship with my bank manager.

On that Saturday evening I drifted off to the local

club for a game of snooker, and had a very enjoyable time too, it being a change from dog books and piles on the floor of local pubs. It must have been around eleven o'clock when I returned home and, as usual, the women were on the telephone taking turns to chatter. After a couple of minutes I politely inquired about whom they were seeking advice from at that late hour.

"Auntie Mary," said Jean, rather sheepishly and it took all of ten seconds for what she had said to sink in.

Auntie Mary lives in New Zealand.

"She lives in bloody Aukland." I roared.

"Hamilton," corrected Jean, "and don't go red in the face dear, we'll soon be finished."

"Too bloody right you will," I howled, "You can't get much further than New Zealand. Next stop's the moon. I suppose we'll be seeking advice from the Yanks in the Sea of Tranquility next."

"You aren't very tranquil, love," Jean remarked as the phone went back on the hook. They both then offered to pay for the call which calmed me down a little, and I slowly subsided into my armchair to be duly ministered upon with cups of tea and a promise not to do it again.

After a few days Auntie Jean went home and we were left surrounded with cardboard boxes, lots of newspapers and vets' telephone numbers written down on scraps of paper, placed at strategic points throughout the house. But Fred knew what she was doing, even if we didn't, and one evening she refused her food.

"That's the first sign," said Jean excitedly. "Now she'll make a bed."

"Great," I said, "can she make Stephen's as well while she's at it. I've just been in his room and it looks as though the England v Scotland match has just been played on it."

"Clever today, aren't we?" Jean replied.

She lined a large cardboard box with newspapers and an old blanket and, partially cutting out a side section to allow entry and exit, showed it to Fred who promptly hopped inside and began knocking hell out of the blanket and paper.

"Don't think she likes it," I said.

"Course she does," retorted Jean. "She's just making her bed aren't you, flower?" she added, patting Fred's head. Fred wagged her tail and carried on ripping.

We all went to bed, Steve being very late as somehow his bedtime had been overlooked in the excitement of Fred's impending motherhood.

"G'night Mum, G'night Dad," he paused before saying his prayers. "Hey, Mum, bet you she has 'em in the night."

"Oh no," I thought. "That's all we need."

Jean was like a jumping jack already and that remark just about put paid to any sleep that night except for Steve and Fred of course. They slept like tops. Jean was up and down stairs like a yoyo 'til the early hours chasing imagined whimpers and cries of pain.

It was perhaps a good thing we were all at home the next day or two, it being half term at school, and I had taken a few days off that were owed to me. The next morning saw Jean and I bleary eyed and Stephen and Fred rarin' to go.

Fred refused even a saucer of milk and about mid-day started to produce puppies.

We had put a box in the hallway where it was reasonably quiet and, while Jean stood guard murmuring words of encouragement, Fred got on with the job. Talk about shelling peas. She was silent as she went through the process of giving birth, cleaning the pups and licking their backs until they gave a little squeak, nipping the cord, disposing of the afterbirth and then starting on the next one. There were six and they were big pups.

But then a small tragedy struck. After five puppies, Fred was showing symptoms of heat and exhaustion. We thought that five was the lot, but fifteen minutes after the birth of the fifth, Fred started up again. It was a breach birth and just too much for her. The pup became firmly stuck, half in and half out and, after a short time, it became obvious even to us that the situation was serious.

Fred lay still, looking up at Jean as she tried to ease the pup out with no success. Eventually she gave up, ran for the telephone and rang the vet.

"Get the pup out," said the vet, "pull and pull, and," he added, "make sure you get the afterbirth as well or she's in trouble. Try now and if you don't get any joy ring me straight back."

So Jean pulled and sweated and pulled again and, slowly at first, the pup came away. It was huge, much bigger than the other five.

Fred lay still as Jean managed to take away the

afterbirth and refused to have anything to do with her latest arrival. We waited for a sign of life but none came. The pup was quite dead. I took the little bundle into the garden and dug another hole beside where Jinx lay. I felt like an undertaker as I went back indoors.

Jean fretted about the pup's size, slandering those people who allow their dogs to wander the streets until I reminded her that it was Fred who had nipped off in search of romance. Then it was all over. We cleaned the box and Fred and then, in a nice clean home, she settled down to feed her five remaining pups, thoroughly exhausted but seemingly happy as her tail twitched a couple of times when I asked her if she was O.K.

Jean grinned at me, "You'd have gone through the roof if she said, 'Yes perfectly, thank you Rog, now clear off'."

I grinned back. "Yeah, I feel like a dad." I said rather foolishly.

She smiled, "You are, love, and your son wants you to play football." Steve and I went out into the sunshine and Jean put on her apron to cook a belated lunch. We were back to normal, or so I thought at the time.

8

Who's the Daddy?

If I was hoping to return to normality after the birth of the litter, this illusion was shattered not twenty-four hours later. That night I had gone out to let all the local lads know what had happened and I realise now that I was partially to blame for what followed.

The queue formed at about nine o'clock the next morning at the back door. Jean had spent the previous evening on the phone so everyone within a fifty mile radius knew Fred had got five pups. I didn't even quibble about the phone bill. Until that morning I never realised what an effect newly born puppies have on even strong men, let alone ladies and, of course, the children... and more children. They came in droves.

I had the notion of serving the queue with tea and buns at a few bob a go, to supplement the beer and fags fund, but this idea was firmly scotched by a severe look from Jean.

One at a time and on tiptoe, the visitors were allowed

a five-second look at the mother and puppies before being escorted away by Jean, who replied in whispers to their solicitous enquiries. Three of the people who came that morning I swear I didn't know from Adam.

Of course we know now that we should not have allowed anyone near her for a few days, but Fred didn't seem to mind and hasn't minded since. She is a gregarious little bitch and I reckon she enjoyed the visits just as much as everybody else did. The children were the most regular visitors apart from Edie, whose household must have ground to a standstill during the first few days following the birth.

One interesting side effect of the affair was an explanation given by Stephen to an assembled group of four, five and six-year-olds about what had happened and how it had happened. Our son had suddenly set himself up as the gynaecological expert and consultant to that age group in our area. As his four eager listeners, two girls and two boys, perched on the fence at the top of the garden, Stephen began his lecture with stunning impact.

"They came out of her bum you know," he said solemnly. Three heads nodded knowingly, the only objector to the truth of the statement being shouted down by the others. After all Stephen had witnessed this wonderful event. At first hand too. So he should know.

Jean giggled and then remarked on the wonderful time the parents were going to have when it came to explaining about the birds and the bees.

"You had better put Steve straight on that sometime, too," I said, "After all you teach biology as well as maths."

"Not on your life," replied Jean, "That's a lad out there and it's a father's job."

But she did eventually. Tell him about the birds and bees, I mean. Me, I'm a coward. And she is a teacher. And teachers aren't cowards. At least, not all of them.

* * *

Fred quickly got back into her stride and Jean informed the vet that his advice had been taken and, more importantly, acted upon with success. When they were about a week old she dumped the pups and Fred, now in a larger box, into the back of the car and carted them off for a visit. The vet looked them over and pronounced them all O.K. and mother O.K. too. Then he arranged for injections and worming and was generally great, dispensing all kinds of advice which we found a lot more useful than all the books we had read. A good lad, that vet. We have gone to the same veterinary practice ever since and, as it turned out later, we made a wise decision.

Newly born puppies cheep like chicks, but as they grow and their eyes open the 'cheep' seems to change into a still very quiet but penetrating squeak. They seem to squeak most when they are hungry, which seems reasonable, but not very reasonable at two o'clock in the morning when I can't sleep. It's amazing how that sound carries in the still hours.

One night, in exasperation, I shouted to Fred to 'Hurry up and feed the little buggers' much to the annoyance of Jean who I awoke in the process. But I reckon Fred must have understood because a couple of minutes later the squeaks subsided and the household went back to sleep. Except for Steve of course. He never even stirred. I reckon that lad could sleep in a steel mill going at full chat.

* * *

"Weaning," said Jean one morning as she lay in bed contemplating the wardrobe.

"Eh?" I mumbled, struggling from sleep.

"Weaning." repeated Jean. "We've got to wean them."

"Eh?"

"The pups, Twit, the pups. Put them on solid food."

"Oh."

There was a long pause.

"Why do you want to wean them at seven o'clock on a Sunday morning?" I inquired. Jean stared at the wardrobe.

"Because it's important."

"Not at seven o'clock on a Sunday morning, it isn't." I said.

"Yes it is," said Jean and hurtled out of bed.

Now this action had been hitherto unknown during all our married life. Jean has crawled, slithered and rolled out of bed, generally appealing to the Almighty, but never had she hurtled. As I have mentioned before Jean is, to say the least, a slow starter in the mornings. She has all the acceleration of a gnat with 50 pound

61

weights strapped to each leg. But this morning was different.

Steve, who was awake, saw her march past his open bedroom door on her way to the bathroom. Stunned to silence for a moment, he quickly recovered and rushed into our bedroom with a look of consternation on his young face.

"Dad, Dad. She's up. Mum's up – before you – what's the matter Dad?"

"Weaning," I said.

"Oh… er… can I get up now?" asked Steve.

"I reckon we'd both better get up," I replied.

"What's weaning, Dad?" he inquired.

"I'm not quite sure, son," I said. "But I've got a feeling that we are about to find out."

What we did find out was that weaning puppies is a highly technical operation. It consists of taking a saucer of mashed up cereal and milk and shoving the pup's head into the mixture. The results of this manoeuvre are exceedingly messy to say the least. The pups are, I am sure, under the impression that weaning is a new game, the object of which is to get covered from head to foot in as much of the food as they can. If, by any coincidence, a minute amount should get into their mouths, this is merely accidental and has nothing to do with the game. There seem to be no particular rules but when 'time' is called, or the game is terminated by the weaner, I think the dirtiest pup is deemed to be the winner.

The first thing they did was to roll on their backs in the saucer, while Fred looked on in approval. Steve and

62

I stood in one corner of the kitchen sniggering, much to Jean's disgust, as she struggled to keep the correct end of the puppy pointing at the food. A couple of them decided it was a public convenience, never having seen one of course, and acted accordingly.

"No! No! No!" screamed Jean and, picking up the saucer, by now almost empty, left Fred to clean them up. Fred wagged her tail as she is quite partial to cereal and milk and within a few minutes all was clean and shipshape again.

But my wife is a very determined lady and refused to be put off by initial failure so, within a couple of hours or so, we were at it again. Again it was slapstick comedy, but after a day or two a couple of them began to get the idea. Shortly afterwards the problem was not to get them to eat but to make sure they all got a fair share. Of course most of them still paddled in the mush but at least most of it went to fill their little stomachs, which were growing bigger all the time.

Fred lost her milk and the pups progressed to finely mashed meat. Many beef casseroles and stews were eaten in our house during that period and, upon Jean's insistence, the leftovers assumed a high proportion of the original dish. These leftovers were then processed with the aid of a fork into highly nutritious puppy food. As I generally add a fairly generous measure of either red wine or beer to our casseroles and stews, I began to fear that they might get a taste for the hard stuff. When a prospective dog owner asks what to feed the little darlings on, you can hardly reply "Guinness and best shin beef".

Puppy feeding time was also a great attraction to the spectators. Those pups got more visitors than a dying millionaire. We began to know what a zoo keeper feels like at feeding time and again I suggested that a small charge might not go amiss, but this was frowned upon so I decided to keep quiet, not wishing to provoke the wrath of wife and son.

My mother and father came to visit us and made the appropriate noises about Fred and the pups. Mum rather likes Fred and, in his way, so does Dad but he has a very ambivalent attitude towards dogs in general. While he freely admits they are man's best friend, he generally likes to keep them at a distance. I rather think that this stems from the time when he was a small boy and used to deliver newspapers for my grandfather who had a rather prosperous newsagent and tobacconist business.

My father, three uncles and my aunt were all, at some time or other, conscripted into the job of delivering the morning papers and all of them seemed to strike up unhappy relationships with dogs in the course of their early morning activities. This seems to have produced a collective family hatred of dogs and, indeed, I have a cousin who refuses to visit us because of Fred's presence in the house. It's either that or the house stinks or something. We are always made most welcome when we visit them, without Fred of course, and are frequently admonished that we do not visit them enough. So I think it is because of Fred. I don't think the house stinks because mother is most keen on that sort of thing and has never been one for being backwards at coming forwards on the subject of smells and their origins. Also, Jean is a bit kinky about cleanliness and would wash the coal before we put it on the fire if I let her. Mind you, it might be because Fred stinks and nobody has got round to noticing it yet.

As the weeks went by, the pups began to assume their colouring and coat and it became increasingly obvious that master Kerry had outfoxed or out-somethinged the rest of Fred's suitors. They were the most beautiful champagne colour with a spiky coat, rough like the Cairn terrier's but with the length and sheen of the Yorkshire. Jean loved them all and postponed the idea of finding homes for them as long as she could. A Crufts champion could have no more loving care and attention given to it than Jean gave those pups. They were all properly wormed, inoculated and vaccinated against everything from hardpad to yellow fever.

But the final highlight to that first litter came for me on the night I walked into the Nags Head and put an end to all the speculation about the identity of the puppies' father. The 'regulars' waited with bated breath as I kept them on the hook and then proudly announced the name and breed. There was much passing of pound notes and pints of bitter that night. In fact, I even got a couple of pints for acting as the impartial judge but, I reflected as I raised my glass, did I really know who the father was? I suspect Fred didn't know either, but then we couldn't ask her, could we?

9

A Rash Holiday

Finding homes for the pups proved easier than I had imagined. Jean was supremely confident right from the start that there would be no problem, and she was right. Since the whole district had received daily bulletins by telephone and word of mouth on the puppies' progress, by the time they were six or seven weeks old we had five or more prospective owners who Jean carefully vetted. I sometimes think that she took more care finding the right kind of home for those cross breeds than she did with subsequent pedigree litters, but maybe that's my imagination.

Only one slight snag occurred and that was the pup which went to Edie. Edie had recently found a job which kept her out of the house for a considerable time each day and, as her husband, Basil, worked shifts the little dog, being left alone, began to fret. The problem was solved when Jean's sister stepped in and offered to take the pup. Edie naturally didn't want to lose him but, at the same time, was quite relieved that he was going to a good home. So we were back to having just Fred in the house and slightly fewer visitors. The silence took some getting used to after all the racket of the past few weeks.

Autumn came, then winter and Fred resumed her position in front of a blazing fire during the long dark evenings.

One evening as we talked, it became apparent that Jean dearly wanted Fred to have some good Yorkie pups so that we could keep one, but we had to face the fact that the little bitch wasn't getting any younger.

"That vet seemed a good fellow," I said, "why don't we consult him about Fred?"

Jean brightened, "Wouldn't do any harm would it?"

The vet gave Fred a thorough examination and said that she was remarkably fit and well and everything would be O.K. provided we didn't leave things too long. "Within the next two seasons" was the advice given, so Jean was very pleased that we had at least a chance to breed her properly, if only just once.

Fred came into season again and this time Jean decided to consult a registered breeder of Yorkshire terriers.

And that's how we met Mrs Samson.

She was a rather dumpy jolly lady in her late fifties and, despite the fact that her hands were crippled with arthritis and must have caused her considerable pain, she always had a kind word for everybody.

Some people walk, others trot or run as they go about their work. Mrs Samson bustled. She was the greatest bustler I have ever seen, never still, always on the go.

Jean made an appointment on the telephone to take Fred to see her and one evening we all piled into the car and drove the four or five miles to the kennels.

Mrs Samson looked at Fred and examined her and then pronounced that she should be mated in a couple of days and who did we prefer as the sire… Muffin or Corky?

Muffin and Corky were the two stud dogs at the kennels and, after much discussion about pedigree and so on between Jean and Mrs Samson, it was decided that Muffin was to be the lucky chap.

Two days later we returned to be met by Mrs Samson and also, this time, by Mr Samson. If his wife bustled, Mr Samson inched his way through life. As we found out, this thoroughly pleasant man had no intention of wearing out his muscles through unnecessary action. The only quick thing about him was his smile. I thought him to be a thoroughly admirable chap.

Muffin was wheeled out and, after a couple of sniffs at Fred, there was no doubt what was on the little fellow's mind.

"Right then," said Mrs Samson, "off we go. Do you want to come, Mr Willgoose?" she asked glancing at me.

"Er… no thank you," I replied, remembering my last efforts as a matchmaker. "I leave it to the experts," I added maliciously, grinning at Jean, who nervously picked up Fred and accompanied Mrs Samson and Muffin down a short path and into a small wooden hut that stood apart from the other buildings. The kennels are set in open countryside and Steve wandered off exploring leaving Mr Samson and me to contemplate the wooden hut.

"They call him Muffin, you know," he began, "because 'e's good at stuffin'." He roared with laughter. "Actually," he said, "it's a good job you came when you did 'cos I reckon 'e's just about knackered 'imself this last three weeks. Mornin', noon and bloody night 'e's at it. Daren't let 'im near the bloody 'ens even. I'm not kiddin', if yon dog were 'uman 'e'd have to be bloody well locked up. Nowt would be safe." I laughed and we talked as we waited.

"I wish 'e'd hurry up," he said eventually, "I've not 'ad any dinner yet." Presently, Mrs Samson emerged from the hut beaming and gave us a little wave. I waved back only to see her disappear again into the hut. I presumed that the wave was a signal that the job had been completed successfully, but Mr Samson offered no explanation. I think he was preoccupied with thoughts of the dinner he hadn't yet had.

Another quarter of an hour passed and then the door of the shed opened and they trooped out. Jean carried Fred and Mrs Samson carried Muffin who looked nothing like as lively as he did when he went in.

"Look at 'im," remarked Mr S. nodding at Muffin, "knackered... 'e'll kill 'is bloody self."

I whistled Steve up and they bade us goodbye and, as the wintry afternoon wore on, we left amid a welter of good advice and good wishes, Jean promising to ring Mrs S. in a few days. I turned the car round and watched them disappear into the house. "I hope he enjoys his dinner," I said.

"What?" inquired Jean, nursing Fred on her knee with a towel held firmly under the dog's rump. I told her about my conversation with Mr Samson.

"It was quite a performance," I said

"Not half the performance we've just had in that shed," replied Jean. "No wonder she had no success when you took her the first time. It's a miracle how they manage it on their own if that lot was anything to go by," Jean explained and we roared with laughter all the way home, Steve joining in, not quite knowing why, but the laugh was to be on me before too long.

* * *

Then came the long wait, Jean willing Fred to be pregnant, but after six weeks had passed it became obvious, much to Jean's disgust, that Fred was carrying nothing more than a full stomach from all the extra high protein food on which she had been fed for the last few weeks.

Many telephone calls had been taking place between Jean and the kennels and Mrs S. told us not to worry and that Fred could have 'a free go' next time she came in season.

After all this frenzied activity we decided it was time for a holiday so, at the end of May, much to Stephen's delight, we set off for a week by the sea.

Between the time of realisation that Fred would not

produce a litter and the start of the holiday, we noticed that she began to scratch herself more than usual. She had always given the occasional flick behind an ear with one of her back legs, but Jean became increasingly worried as the scratching became more prolonged. A first inspection revealed nothing but, as the days went by, further examination showed a slight pinkish rash forming on her back and sides and behind her ears.

"It's fleas! I know it's fleas," cried Jean. "She's got them off that Muffin."

"If it is, it's about the only thing she did get off him," I replied, "unless you count… "

"Shut up!" yelled Jean. "It's the vet's for you tomorrow, Madam," and she continued looking worriedly at Fred.

If it were not for the fact that veterinary surgeons extract a fee for each visit, I would have thought that the bloke we went to see was beginning to get a bit fed up of seeing Fred at what seemed every verse end. Not a bit of it though. He carefully examined her and then pronounced that she had a rash. To his everlasting credit, he added that he didn't know what the hell it was that caused it. Some people may find this strange but when he said that my opinion of his ability increased. I like people who admit when they don't know something because I'm always having to do it myself. I'm in a business where everybody pretends to know everything about everything all of the time and it's very refreshing and reassuring to meet someone who says, "I don't know". He told us what he thought it might be and

71

when Jean said that we were shortly going for a holiday by the sea he brightened immediately.

"Tell you what," he said, "chuck her in the sea and we'll see what happens."

We have some friends who, at that time, kept a small hotel in a seaside town on the East Coast. They are a wonderful couple and nothing is too much trouble for them. I was a little dubious about taking Fred, but they said that if she didn't go we need not bother going either, so that seemed to settle the matter.

The hotel is slap bang on the sea front and Steve, as usual, was in his seventh heaven. The weather was kind and at the first opportunity we invaded the beach and Fred thought it was her birthday. She dashed and scampered in the sand, digging holes and sending sand and pebbles flying in all directions, chasing Steve and then letting him chase her.

"Hey," said Jean, turning to me as we watched her antics in amazement. "I know why… she's never seen the sea before." It was a fact that neither of us had realised. Even Steve was amazed at her cavorting among the sand and, to our slight embarrassment, the assembled sunbathers. The previous summer we had left her with Jean's sister while we took a holiday and, as she had never been taken to the seaside while she lived with Auntie Jean, this was her first trip. And did she make the most of it? When it came to 'chucking her into the sea' we didn't have to. She dashed headlong into the waves and, as her initial momentum was gradually slowed by the incoming tide, sat down letting the water wash over her. She trotted back to us, tail going like a metronome, looking like an apology for a weasel. Steve dashed into the water and she swiftly gave chase, stopping only when the waves splashed over her.

"Hard work, that," said Jean, turning to me as we watched the pair of them.

"Eh?" I said.

"Chucking her into the sea like the vet said," remarked Jean, grinning.

"Yeh, wasn't it… er… are you going in?"

"Might," said Jean. "What about you?"

"Paddle," I said, rolling up my battered jeans, "Want to go beachcombing."

"Coward," said Jean taking off her skirt and sweater to reveal a bikini. She charged into the sea to join Stephen but Fred, now weary from her exertions, joined me and we paddled up and down the shoreline looking for shells. Fred found a small crab and came to me holding it by a claw and dubiously presenting it for inspection.

"Great," I said, "it's a crab." Fred wagged her tail. It was a very little crab.

The initial attraction of the sand and sea was shortly superseded by the counter attraction of the cocktail bar of the hotel, in Fred's book, at least. Here was heaven on earth for a little dog skilled in the art of looking mournful and hungry. Peter, the proprietor, said afterwards that the sale of nuts and crisps had doubled during the time we were there. What never ceases to amaze me is the fact that people who are ordinarily well balanced become disorientated when faced with a small dog with a wagging tail. It's no use at all to tell them that the dog is well fed and may accept a small titbit. The only passion in the lives of the occupants of that bar seemed to be to give Fred as many nuts and crisps as they could.

At one stage it seemed to develop into a covert competition as to who could stuff the most down her in the shortest time. We called a halt on the fourth day, which happened to be the second evening running that she had gone out on to the promenade, thrown up in the gutter, and then gone back for more. This might seem to indicate that we were not taking as much care of our dog as we should. Not so, half the time we couldn't bloody well find her. The other residents had formed a kind of Mafia from which, of course, we were excluded. The object of this clandestine organisation was to feed Fred without our knowledge and after a while I began to feel like Edgar J. Hoover. Reasoning with them was no good at all. They all smiled, nodded and agreed wholeheartedly with the arguments we put forward, then they pinched Fred when we went up to the bar for a drink and stuffed her full of nuts and crisps.

But her rash disappeared completely. Now I don't know whether it was the sea water or the nuts and crisps. We've got a super vet and he and Jean say it was the sea water. And I suppose they must be right.

Or are they?

10

House Bricks and Vaseline

We did not seem to have been home from the holiday for five minutes before Fred came into season again. It was neck or nothing this time because Jean had made up her mind that if no pups were forthcoming then Fred was to be 'retired' from breeding; always assuming, of course, that she didn't nip off on one of her amorous adventures with one or more of the local canine Casanovas.

So this time everyone was very careful about closing doors and gates. Even Steve remembered occasionally, usually when Jean ordered him to do so in her best schoolmarm voice.

Daily inspections were made of the appropriate parts of Fred's anatomy and then the phone calls began once more to Mrs Samson. These telephone discussions got very technical, not to say faintly disgusting, until Jean made a great decision.

"Saturday," she announced. "It's Saturday. We think all the signs point to Saturday as the optimum for mating."

"Good," I replied without much interest, studying the cricket score in the morning paper.

"So you can take her on Friday," said Jean.

"Hold on a minute," I started, "I thought you said Saturday. What sort of cockeyed feminine logic is it that tells you I'm to take her on Friday?"

"Because I'm at school and it's your day off," replied Jean.

"That's bloody stupid," I said, "she's ready to be mated on Saturday so we take her on Friday… sit down love and have a glass of something strong, you're going round the twist, or I am."

"It's only to look," said Jean, as though explaining to a two-year-old. "You take her tomorrow so Mrs Samson can look at her, then you bring her home and then I take her on Saturday for the mating… See?"

"That's daft," I began, "why don't we just leave it 'til Saturday. We didn't have to take her for an inspection last time, did we?"

"No… and we didn't get any bloody pups either, did we… ?" she yelled. So, as you can see, I lost the argument and to this day I can't really understand why. Anyway, it was all a fiendish feminine plot.

On Friday morning Jean smiled a lot and said that Mrs S. expected me about ten o'clock. She and Steve drove off to school, leaving me with Fred and the attendant mongrels in the garden hoping against hope, no doubt, that somebody would leave the back door open again.

Fred was bursting with life and energy, she seemed

to have enough for both of us, which was just as well as four of us fellows had done our best to drink the Chequers Hotel dry of bitter the previous evening on the pretext of celebrating the return from Scotland of the landlord, Stuart, who had been on a reasonably successful salmon fishing trip. Stuart is one of my best and oldest friends but when we are in each other's company, which is very often, things tend to get out of hand somewhat. Stuart's wife, Ethel, and Jean also get along very well and have formed a sort of secret society to prevent these occasions, but they don't seem to meet with much success.

This left me that morning with a banging hangover, a Yorkshire terrier bitch in heat and a Rover 2000 which would not start. One thing I had eventually found out about that car was that swearing at it was no good. It only responded to a quiet chat, so I chatted and eventually and very reluctantly the car spluttered into life… just as I was mentally composing a snotty letter to British Leyland.

We arrived at the kennels at smack on ten o'clock to be met by a beaming Mrs Samson.

"Good, good, good," she chortled as she bustled up to the car and, barely waiting for me to get out, snatched up Fred and inspected her backside. "Oh yes, very good, very good indeed," she went on, after her inspection. "Right then, we'll get on with it."

"Get on with what?" I asked, panic rising and overcoming the hangover.

"The mating, of course, the mating." She called over her shoulder, "I'll get Muffin."

"But… but Jean said it was only to… " I called feebly after her.

"Yes, I know," shouted back Mrs Samson, "but there's no time like the present is there?" Nobody argues with Mrs Samson. It's impossible. She doesn't stand still long enough. The hangover mixed in with the panic and I felt awful as I hung on to Fred. Then rage took over.

"I've been done," I thought. "That bloody wife of mine has set me up for this… I'll kill her when I get home… I bet she's laughing her socks off… I hope all the kids in her class throw up this morning."

Mrs Samson returned with Muffin and a look of pity crossed her face. "You needn't come into the 'boudoir' if you don't want to," she smiled. Taking a look at my eyes she said, "Yes, perhaps you had better stay out here."

They all went off down the path to the shed, the two dogs sniffing each other eagerly, and waves of relief flooded over me. "Great," I thought. "Got out of it." The hangover symptoms subsided slightly.

A minute later the shed door opened and Mrs Samson rushed out past me and into the house. Ten seconds later she re-appeared clutching a tin of Vaseline and a house brick. Now I've heard about these kinky activities and I had a rough idea of what the Vaseline was for, but bloody house bricks! Mrs Samson must have read my thoughts.

"It's for him to stand on while he does it," she explained, disappearing once again into the hut. "He's only little you see," she called over her shoulder as the door closed.

After about a quarter of an hour a telephone began to ring in the house and in a few minutes the door of the hut opened and a flushed Mrs Samson beckoned to me.

"I need help," she shouted.

"What help am I going to be?" I thought as I trailed down the path.

"Now then," said Mrs Samson as she met me at the door. "It's all over bar the shouting but it's important that they don't part yet." I looked down and saw Fred and Muffin tied together in their lovers embrace. "Hold their heads and don't let them part. I have to answer the phone. Muffin will try to get away but don't let him," was her parting shot as she shut me in the hut with the dogs, after showing me how to hold their heads. The place was spotlessly clean and bare apart from a tin of Vaseline and a house brick.

I crouched down holding the dogs' heads as instructed, cursing Jean and telephones in turn. After about ten minutes the hangover re-asserted itself and I got cramp in my right leg. I tried sitting on the house brick but that seemed to make matters worse.

After about twenty minutes I was ready to commit suicide. I'd got cramp in both legs now and Muffin had tried to bite me twice.

Presently I heard footsteps and, still holding their heads, struggled to look through the small window in the side of the shed. I saw Mrs Samson talking to one of the kennel maids. She appeared to be quite unhurried and the two of them started walking slowly back towards the house deep in conversation.

"Can I come out now?" I yelled at the top of my voice. Mrs Samson turned, the dogs parted and Muffin had another go at my hand.

"Oh dear," said Mrs Samson, opening the door. "I'd quite forgotten about you. A few minutes would have been quite sufficient. Still never mind, you've done very well, haven't you?" she beamed.

I tried to stand up and fell over. The legs had gone. I wasn't sure where the head was either. But it is almost impossible to be angry with Mrs Samson. One little smile took all the wind out of my sails and, as I managed to stand upright, I thanked her for all she had done and, bidding her farewell, I took Fred to the car making a mental note to beat Jean to death when she got back from school. The whole thing had lasted less than an hour.

The pain eased slightly from my legs as I drove slowly home with Fred curled on the back seat on a dog blanket. She had a self satisfied smile on her face and every now and again made little contented grunting noises. I was glad somebody felt happy. All I had got that morning was a banging head, albeit self-inflicted, and a pair of aching legs.

Working on the theory that 'what makes you bad makes you better', I walked up the road to the Chequers at lunchtime after dropping Fred and the car off at home.

That was another mistake.

Ethel was in the bar and, after taking one look, asked me if I'd mind going outside to die as it might put the lunchtime trade off their beer if I dropped dead at the bar and, by the look of me, it was quite possible.

Further cracks followed about over indulgence.

"Anyway, it's your own fault," said Ethel," if it's any consolation Stu' wasn't too clever this morning either, but he's O.K. now."

"He's not been bent double in a bloody shed with a pair of sex-mad dogs." I replied.

"What *have* you been doing?" asked Ethel. So I told her.

I should have kept my mouth shut. Anyone with a hangover is a figure of fun, but somebody with a hangover, aching in both legs and telling as highly unlikely story as mine becomes the butt for every joke in the pub.

And then, of course, there are all the wise men with hangover cures.

"Double brandy, cider and gin," said one. "That'll do the trick… never fails. 'Ere, give 'im one, Ethel, all in a big glass mind. I'll pay."

"You bloody well won't," I interrupted. I struggled on with a pint of Bass, sipping slowly and pulling faces from time to time much to the amusement of the lunchtime regulars.

Stu' stuck his head round the door, said, "How do, Rog," took one look at me and hurriedly disappeared.

Wise man, that Stuart.

I began to feel a little better and consoled myself with the thought of tearing into Jean when she got home from school. Then some idiot bought me another pint.

So the lunchtime hour stretched out somewhat and by the time I went home I felt at peace with the world and when Jean got back from school I could no more have summoned up any anger than I could have jumped over the house. I felt like Muffin… knackered.

However, I did manage a token protest but Jean saw it for what it was. Grinning hugely she walked into the kitchen where I was preparing the evening meal, as I do on my days off when she is teaching. I have a rather beautiful French chef's knife. It's about fourteen inches long and as sharp as a razor. I had had great plans for that evening concerning the knife and Jean, but I slowly put the knife down as Jean beamed.

"Well love, how did it go?" She put down her briefcase and picked up Fred, stroking and cooing gently.

"You know bloody well how it went," I snarled quietly. "You and Mrs Samson… set me up, didn't you?"

Wide eyed in astonishment, feigned or actual, I have never been sure, Jean turned to me.

"Why, love?"

"'Cos I'm near enough bloody crippled, aren't I?" I complained. "And don't give me any bull about you not knowing what happened."

"What did happen, love?" asked Jean. "Look, I'll get us both a drink and you can tell me all about it." So I was led into the sitting room and, with a glass of lemonade in my hand, told my story, warming to it as I got to the bits about my sufferings. Jean giggled most of the way through but when I finished she said,

"Great, so she's been mated. How clever of that Mrs Samson to know when it was time, you just took her at the right moment, but… " and here she turned to me wide-eyed once again and reached for my hand, "I didn't know it would be today. Mrs S. said tomorrow."

What do you say? What do you do?

Steve came in from school and Jean dished up the evening meal.

"Had a good day, son?" I asked.

"Yeh, I got two team points at school today... You had a good day, Dad?"

"I'm not quite sure really," I replied. "but I know I didn't get any team points."

11

Proper Pups

Jean's slowness to get going in the morning is occasionally accompanied by sudden outbursts of sheer bad temper. The smallest thing going wrong can sometimes spark this off but it is usually over as quickly as it starts. I understand a lot of ladies are like this but, only ever having been married to one, I can make no comparisons. Thank the Lord.

On these occasions Jean seems to believe that the whole day before her will be one long battle against unknown malevolent forces and both Steve and I have been accused of bringing on these bouts of violent melancholy.

Now I know that it is rather upsetting to have a boisterous seven-year-old boy singing selections from the Top Twenty at six o'clock on a Saturday morning when all good school teachers should be allowed at least another two, if not three, hours' sleep, but I fail to see how a couple of quiet verses of Onward Christian Soldiers, sung by a loving husband while he is in the bathroom, can provoke the same reaction.

For the most part, Steve and I ignore what we consider to be feminine tantrums as we know they will subside before long and consider that it is our manly task to uphold whatever dignity is left to the household. Besides that, we enjoy going downstairs and talking about 'the lady in the top loft' in voices just loud enough for the odd word to be heard on the top floor.

For some reason or other this provokes more anger in the patient which seems to hasten the healing process; a good thing for all concerned. These outbursts usually happen at weekends and by the time the lady descends, bacon, eggs and fried bread are on the table with fruit juice and lots of scalding tea. Nothing restores Jean's good humour like a full stomach and very soon we are all getting along famously again.

Steve and I are never nasty tempered of course, because men don't do that sort of thing. Jean and my mother, and my mother-in-law for that matter, violently disagree but, as Steve points out, they are only jealous. I have great hopes for that boy.

But Fred was not privy to these unspoken agreements about Jean's temper. I suppose it was because she was a lady herself. In short she was terrified when Jean let rip. She would shiver and shake and go round wetting the carpets until Jean calmed down. If the door was open she was away, sometimes round to Jean's mother's house which is not too far off. Usually she would shoot off up the lane in the opposite direction or hide out in the garage until things quietened down. As she has now aged considerably and taken on a more mature attitude to life, she joins in with Stephen and me, which secretly pleases Jean as one of those outbursts nearly ended in catastrophe, but that comes later.

One Sunday morning, shortly after Fred's visit to the kennels, Jean had experienced one of her traumatic moments and, as she lay in bed steaming with wrath, we went downstairs to make breakfast. We kept the kitchen door shut and put Fred outside so that she could shiver and pee on the garden for a change. When she was left in the house we always noted where the dark patches were and left them for Jean to clear up when she appeared. This was a penance which seemed particularly appropriate and, to her everlasting credit, Jean cleaned up after Fred with hot water and disinfectant and with only a minimum of protest.

But in these weeks, following her affair with Muffin, Fred was in no hurry to run away from home. I think this had something to do with the fact that once again she was living off the fat of the land. Apart from the usual meat and meal; milk, fish and eggs were added to her diet as Jean willed her to produce some pedigree Yorkie pups. Fred thought the whole thing was marvellous, a 'love 'em and leave 'em' affair followed by stacks of wonderful grub. And they call it a dog's life.

The eggs were not the sort you get from a supermarket either. We have about forty dozen from a nearby farm each fortnight, with Jean doing the buying for ourselves and our friends. We live six miles away from a city but are right on the edge of open countryside which stretches for miles and miles. So we seem to get the best of both worlds;

the countryside providing fresh eggs, poached game and beautiful walks and the city for big holes in the bank balance due to Jean's frequent assaults on the houses of haute couture. Getting back to the eggs, I reckon our farmer has a secret flock of ostriches as I'm sure no ordinary hens can lay eggs of such size and quality. But, of course, he's a Derbyshire lad and he turns a deaf ear to all enquiries and we just eat the eggs.

At least Fred was eating the eggs at that time; and the meat, and the fish and drinking all the milk.

"She's pregnant," beamed Jean one day, holding Fred upside down in her lap. "Look how her tummy's swelling."

"No she ain't," said Steve, rather coarsely, "it's all that extra grub she's having."

"What do you think?" Jean looked at me rather anxiously. "Look, she is a bit heavy, isn't she?" I peered at Fred's upturned tum as she lay in Jean's lap, wagging her tail and waving her legs in the air.

"Er... ah... well. Slightly pregnant, I think," I replied.

"Oh good," said Jean

"Don't be daft." I answered, "I haven't got the faintest idea. Maybe Steve's right and it's just the grub.

Jean sighed, "Well, we should know in a couple of weeks." Jean was beside herself with delight at the thought of breeding a litter of 'proper pups'.

"The last lot were proper pups," said Steve.

"Yes of course they were, darling," Jean replied, "but not as beautiful as these will be... I hope," she added glancing at me.

"Well," I said, "she did O.K. with the last lot, so there's no reason to suppose she won't do as well with these." Jean was showing all the symptoms of the expectant grandmother.

Despite her increasing size, Fred in no way became lethargic. If anything her energy increased and she began to adapt an over protective attitude to the house and family. She has always been a good guard dog, warning us of the approach of strangers with a few barks and sometimes a growl. Fred never yaps. Indeed, sometimes her growls are so low and fierce that I look over my shoulder to make sure I am not being followed by an Alsatian.

She has never really taken to dustmen. The weekly arrival of the refuse collectors is met with a frenzy of barks and growls and a general 'let me get at 'em' attitude. The milkman and the postman do not seem to merit such ferocious attention; just a warning that the milk and mail have been delivered. This has always mystified me as our dustmen are a jolly bunch of chaps and we always stop for a chat if I am at home when they call. But in Fred's book they are intruders to be repelled as quickly as possible. Perhaps it's because she thinks they are stealing something when they take the dustbins away to be emptied.

One day this over-protectiveness stretched to nipping the heels of a young man delivering advertising pamphlets and free offer coupons. I have very fixed views on liberties taken by the advertising media but it does not stretch to biting people's legs off when they push the blurb through our letter box. So Fred was suitably admonished. I was just about to kick her up the backside when Jean frantically reminded me of her 'condition'. I gave Fred a stern lecture. After ensuring that the young man could still walk, the only result was a wagging tail and, what I took to be, the self-satisfied expression of someone secure in the knowledge of a job well done.

"She's just making sure that the house is safe for her to have her pups," said Jean.

"Why didn't she do it the last time?" I protested

"Ah, but, this is different... this time... " and here I joined in, "they are proper pups." Jean said a naughty word and I gave up. After all, she was probably right. Women generally are.

Preparations began for the whelping (Jean was picking up the canine terminology) with more cardboard boxes and, of course, the compulsory pile of newspapers. Jean had run short of newspapers when Fred had her previous litter and had been reduced to scurrying round to friends for any unwanted papers they could provide. She had decided that no such crisis should arise on this occasion and, as she lay in the accumulated reading matter of four or five households, our kitchen and living room began to resemble the publishing department of the Daily Telegraph.

We acquired a whelping blanket which, for the uninitiated, is soft and fluffy and absorbent and hellish expensive for a couple of square feet of glorified nylon. But there would be no second best for Fred this time.

This time we knew what we were doing. This time they would be real Yorkshire terrier pups.

"Next stop Crufts," I remarked to Steve one day as we surveyed Jean's elaborate preparations. I was reminded of the water rat in The Wind in the Willows equipping the badger, mole and toad with a great variety of firearms and other offensive weapons for the assault on Toad Hall. The preparation was perfect. Now we awaited the actual performance.

On Sunday, shortly before she was due to whelp, Fred threw the whole set up out of gear by disappearing for a couple of hours. This time there was no provocation, no tantrums from Jean. Indeed, the house that day was a model of tranquillity until somebody noticed that Fred was missing.

Frantic telephone calls were made to Jean's mother, Edie and various other neighbours, but the reply was always the same. No sign of Fred.

After a search of the immediate vicinity of the house, it became apparent that Fred had taken it into her head to go for a walk alone. Jean got out her car and toured the neighbourhood searching but, again, drew a blank.

After half an hour Jean was back home and ringing the police, reporting the loss of a pregnant Yorkshire terrier bitch, and yes, she was wearing a collar. The Yorkshire terrier bitch that is, although I remarked at the time that it would not be a bad idea if women... but I was quickly rebuked by Jean for my levity in what could only be described (Jean's words) as a time of great distress.

We waited and waited until Jean suddenly jumped up in an even more agitated state.

"I know what she's done," she cried, "she's gone away to have them, she's so near now and perhaps she doesn't trust us after we let all those visitors in to see the other pups. She's scared and wants to protect them."

"Rubbish," I replied, but I made the statement more out of a desire to comfort Jean than out of conviction. "Anyway, love, she'll come back for her food, she always does."

It was Steve who came up with the idea of taking a walk around the park. Near the house we have a recreation ground which is referred to locally as 'The Park'. It has a pavilion, a couple of football pitches, a cricket pitch and a bowling green and is altogether a rather pleasant place.

"Well," said Jean, "we aren't doing much good sitting here." So we walked rather disconsolately to search the Park.

Small boys and girls, accompanied by a fair smattering of dogs, raced around the boundary of a cricket pitch much to the annoyance of the cricketers who were engaged in a Sunday afternoon fixture. But none of the dogs remotely resembled Fred. We turned to the small children's playground past the notice all dogs ignore which states that 'dogs are not permitted in this area'. But, as the children and dogs raced about the swings, slide and see-saw, we could see no sign of our now very severely pregnant Yorkshire terrier bitch.

It was when we came to the bowling green that Jean

let out what can only be described as a muted whoop. Relief, concern and annoyance were bottled up in that cry as we saw Fred. She was sitting on the bank beside the green calmly watching the men in white as they bowled away the sunny summer afternoon. Jean called her softly and, tail twitching, Fred calmly trotted across to us.

"Oh it's yours, is it?" remarked an old gentleman who was sitting on one of the seats surrounding the grass. "Good as gold, that dog. Likes bowls. She's watched all afternoon." Jean picked her up and we nodded and smiled to everyone as we made our way home.

"I can't understand why she did it," said Jean, as a much happier family left the park.

"You did some funny things when you were pregnant," I replied. "I remember when you… "

"Yes… well," cut in Jean, "but she didn't do it last time."

"Ah," I said, "but she wasn't having proper pups then, was she?"

12

Charlie Girl

The deep copper coloured lightning which slashed down, seeming only to just miss the house, was followed almost instantaneously by the ear cracking smash of thunder, which showed that the centre of the storm was almost overhead. The clouds had been gathering for over an hour and what had started out as a clear blue, hot summer's day had turned into the blue blackness of near night, although it was only the middle of the afternoon. After the first few heavy drops, the rain pelted down with unbelievable intensity, bouncing off the paths and roads in a steady roar.

Ordinarily, we don't mind thunder storms. Stephen, indeed, considers them to be something of a bonus as the lane by our house becomes a torrent of water running down the slight incline. Fred usually accompanies him as he perches on the wide windowsill to watch the storm and shows no sign of alarm.

But today was different. In her usual obliging manner, Fred had begun to have her puppies in the afternoon, not wishing to inconvenience anybody by keeping unsocial hours. As she began bearing the first pup, the thunder had crashed above us and her terror was apparent as she staggered round the box dragging her half born offspring with her.

Jean was marvellous, doing her best to calm Fred and at the same time trying to help her part with the puppy.

Eventually, Fred lay still and, for almost half an hour, shivered as she struggled to expel the puppy aided by Jean. At last she succeeded and, as the storm passed over and the force of the rain diminished, she set about cleaning up the puppy and methodically settled down to having another four. After the distressing start there were no more hitches and, an hour and a half later, she was settling down to feed five hungry puppies as they squealed and fought blindly to find her teats.

Jean began playing the proud grandmother again and we all heaved a sigh of relief after the traumas of electric storms and puppy births at the same time.

Pinfold Lane was awash, the water lifting the storm drain cover from its seating as it cascaded over the road in a frothing mass four or five inches deep. Several cars had been halted by the storm and the wash of water so Steve and I went out to see what we could do to help. As often happens after a summer storm of such violence, the blue skies seemed to quickly push away the black wedge of cloud and by late afternoon the sun beat down again raising water vapour from the roads and hopes in the drivers of the stopped cars as, one by one, their engines dried out and they set off again.

All in all, Steve thought it had been a most satisfactory day with its share of tension, drama and violence which is so beloved of small boys, provided they are not directly involved and can be treated to a grandstand view. But, as we went back to the house, I noticed that Jean had a very concerned look on her face.

"What's the matter, love?" I enquired.

"I'm not quite sure… yet," replied Jean. "It's perhaps too early to tell, but I have a funny feeling that Fred is rejecting that first pup. It's so much smaller than the others and every time it gets to the teat she pushes it away. At least I think she does, perhaps it's my imagination. Anyway, we'll see if she will let him feed when the others are full."

Fred didn't. Every time the little puppy got near a teat she contemptuously kicked it away with her back leg or stood up so that he could not reach her.

This state of affairs persisted for the next twenty four hours. The other four puppies were fed and cleaned but when it came to 'Tiny', as Jean had called the little dog, Fred just didn't want to know. The only way that the little chap got any nourishment at all was when Jean held Fred down and, pushing the other pups away, held Tiny to a teat and let him drink his fill. Fred protested violently at first but, catching the look in my eye as I watched the proceedings, allowed Jean to get on with the job of trying to rear a very small and hungry puppy.

After a few days it became obvious that we were fighting a losing battle. When Jean was present and could help the pup to feed, the little fellow drank his fill, but puppies feed at every odd hour of the day and night and, in our absence, Fred was refusing to have anything to do with him.

Jean rang the vet and explained about the thunderstorm and Tiny being the first pup and Fred's refusal to feed him,

"Bring him down and I'll have a look," he said. So Jean put Tiny in a small shoe box lined with soft towelling and set off to drive the three or four miles to the surgery. I must confess I was furious with Fred and admonished her severely while Jean was gone, going even so far as to wag my finger at her. Twice.

At the back of my mind were the stories about the bitch always rejecting the sickly and feeble so that only the strong should survive and I had almost reconciled myself to this argument when Jean returned with Tiny.

"There's nothing wrong with him," Jean stated. "The vet says he is a small Yorkie pup and is lacking mother's milk and he says if Fred won't feed him we must. He's given me this." She held up a small glass dropper with a bulb on the end.

"Ostermilk," said Steve brightly.

"Eh?" replied Jean.

"That's what I had when I was little like him," he said, pointing to Tiny.

"The vet said we should try Lactol. I'll see he gets a feed from Fred when I'm around," said Jean, "and we'll see how it goes."

For the next few days Jean worked at keeping Tiny alive and he relished the times when she held him to Fred's teats so that he could feed, but success was less marked with the dropper. However, he was getting nourishment and, although he was so small and not as strong as the other puppies, he fought for life despite the rejection by his mother.

We thought that Fred might come round and accept that the little dog, born at the height of the storm, was hers, but she still stubbornly refused to have anything to do with him. The other four puppies, two dogs and two bitches, thrived and grew; opening their eyes after a couple of weeks and, much to our surprise and delight, Tiny's eyes opened a couple of days later.

Jean took him to the vet again and we were encouraged to keep up the fight.

He fought and scrambled with the other bigger pups. We had tried keeping him apart from them but his strength ebbed and he seemed to prefer to continue his struggle for life in the company of the others.

One evening Jean noticed him lying in a corner of the box while the other puppies fed from Fred's swollen teats. She got the dropper and, taking the small body in her hand, began to feed him with small drips. But there was no interest, no sign of hunger, though he had certainly had nothing from Fred. Jean kept trying but he would not even open his mouth.

"He needs warmth," said Jean sadly. "They have all rejected him." She took the small shoe box which had once contained a pair of sandals bought for Stephen and, lining it with towelling again, gently placed Tiny in it. Setting it on the hearth before the fire, Jean sat with him for four hours.

I buried him at midnight under a rose bush in the front garden. He had hardly moved after the last attempted feed at about eight o'clock and, as we kept watch over him, his strength ebbed and died. He had fought and struggled to the end but had lost his fight.

Perhaps Fred knew that he had no chance to live. Perhaps it would have been kinder of us to have killed him quickly once we knew she had rejected him. But the will to live is strong and at least we hoped that we had done all we could with our limited knowledge for that little dog.

The four remaining puppies and Fred were getting on just fine. Jean had taken the pups to have their tails docked. We have very mixed feelings about what is a controversial operation in many breeds. In order to sell the puppies we *had* to have the tails docked, but I wonder who started the fashion in the first place and why the showing organisations insist that it be done. I have no little sympathy with animal lovers who oppose this procedure and I am inclined to agree with them, that if God had not wanted dogs to have tails they would be born with the stumps that docking leaves. I honestly don't know any reason for it, apart from the dictates of fashion.

I know of one vet who insists that the pup owners should watch the operation. This tends to reduce the enthusiasm of the owner, particularly if they are of a sympathetic nature towards the animals concerned.

Docking or no docking, they thrived and soon began to develop little personalities of their own. One little dog, who was eventually to go to some friends, had a very pugnacious attitude towards the others, while his smaller brother was the noisiest pup we had ever bred. The two bitches, one slightly bigger than the other, sometimes behaved like little ladies but more often than not joined in the general brawling at feeding time. Fred had plenty of 'milk bars' operational but they all seemed to prefer the same teat, so there was a great deal of pushing and shoving at mealtimes.

The visiting arrangements were very much as before, but we did manage to keep the rush of visitors away until the puppies' eyes were open.

I suppose that little dogs are at their most attractive when they eventually begin to walk. About this time Yorkies, who are born with smooth hair, begin to develop a spiky look as their coats grow and it's a real hard case who cannot summon up some sort of affection for them at this stage.

For a few days I had noticed my wife casting longing and affectionate looks in the direction of the larger of the two bitches and wondered how long it would take her to broach the subject of keeping it. Seldom, if ever, does Jean come straight to the point. There is always a preamble which can go on for days and may, initially, only have a very faint bearing on what materialises a few hours or days later. It's the old story at our house. If you want to sample the product, you have to listen to the advertising first. I don't really mind as I usually tumble to whatever it is that Jean is trying to get at and this knowledge gives me a little bit of help when we get down to discussing the matter in hand. And, when arguing with Jean about something on which her mind is really set, I need all the help I can get.

So I resigned myself in advance to the fact that we would shortly have a permanent staff of two Yorkshire terrier bitches, and I secretly gave the new addition to the family a name, after due consultation with Stephen,

There was a great deal of 'advertising' from Jean, who eventually made the proposition, and I think she was a little surprised when I kept agreeing with every statement she made as she went through the carefully rehearsed introduction.

"She might die, you know... she's getting on now and if she did we would be left... er, well... dogless," went on Jean trying, I thought, to kill off Fred prematurely in her desperation to keep a puppy. "Anyway we need another bitch to breed from now that Fred has done her stuff. Continue the line and so forth." I nodded, silently reflecting on the vast fortunes to be made from breeding puppies.

To anyone wishing to breed pups from a single bitch in order to make money, I can give a word of advice. Don't. You won't make a penny. By the time you have paid out for extra food, stud fees, registration fees and all the paraphernalia that goes with a litter of pups you will be lucky to break even. The outlay I have just mentioned does not include your own time and the petrol used shunting the mother and pups about. So if you are in it for the money... forget it.

But Jean had the bit firmly between her teeth and

seemed to be determined to use every argument at her disposal to ensure that we kept the particular puppy she had selected. I must have overdone the agreeing as Jean became suspicious and, hurriedly for her, came to the point. I agreed again, adding that I thought it was a wonderful idea, wondering at the same time if I could keep my face straight any longer. I couldn't, and burst out laughing to be immediately joined by Jean.

"It's the big bitch isn't it?" I asked.

"Yes. Oh great, that's settled then," replied Jean. "Now then," she continued, "about a name for her, I was thinking of something like… "

"She's already got one." I interrupted.

"Oh no," wailed Jean. "You positively are not calling her 'Herbert' or anything like that."

"Certainly not," I answered, "Steve and I have had high level talks and we have come up with something that we believe will be acceptable to everybody, er… including the doggie." Steve, who knows better than to interrupt at summit conferences, nodded.

"What?" asked Jean ominously, "is this wonderful name?"

"Charlie." I picked up the paper and hid from the storm.

"We can't call her Charlie," howled Jean. "Good grief, Fred and Charlie… it sounds like two of your boozy mates. Whoever heard of a girl named Charlie?"

"We've got a girl named Fred," I replied. "Anyway haven't you ever heard of 'Charlie Girl'?" Jean slowly subsided. "Well, perhaps Charlotte."

"Oh you are stupid, the pair of you." She glanced at Steve and me. "Fred and Charlie, my mother always said there was something not quite right in the head about you, and he's just about as bad." She nodded at Stephen.

"She can have a posh kennel name," I offered.

Jean brightened immediately and after deep thought announced her findings. That's how we got the latest permanent addition to our little family... Pinfold Charlie Girl.

* * *

"We need one of those cages you make compost in," said Jean one morning.

"Great," I thought. I had been hanging my nose over a compost maker for a while, as the price of bags of the stuff had been rising steadily for some time, and the rate I used peat and compost in the garden was making it an increasingly expensive hobby.

"That's very kind and thoughtful of you, love. I'll buy a bag of that stuff you mix with the grass cuttings and kitchen waste and so forth to help it rot, and we're in business. Save me a packet that," I finished as I mopped up the last of the egg from my breakfast plate.

"We are not 'in business' as you put it," replied Jean. "It's not for you, it's for the puppies." I stared at her.

"What the hell are puppies going to do with a compost cage?" I inquired.

"They are going to live in it." Jean smiled. "We put them in the cage out on the lawn and they can enjoy the sunshine and we don't have to worry about them running away or getting into trouble or anything. We can lift the cage into the hall and all their little bodily functions can be restricted to one small area which will be much more hygienic and convenient for all."

"What bodily functions?" chipped in Steve.

"Lavatory jobs, dimwit," I answered.

"Well, if she meant… "

"Shut up, Steve," said his mother sharply. So Jean got out her car and, leaving Steve and me to do the washing up, set off in the Saturday morning rain to do the weekend shopping and, presumably, to buy a compost cage.

An hour and a half later she returned with the shopping, but no cage. The local hardware stores were sold out of them it seemed. As always in times of great stress and frustration, Jean retired to the telephone intent, it seemed, on inflating the bill and scouring the length and breadth of two counties in search of a compost cage that doubled as a dog pen. Later questioning revealed that the idea had come from a friend who bred dogs and had such a device which she apparently used with great success. But, despite the frantic use of the telephone and an afternoon tour of the district's garden shops, no cage was to be had. This had rather a depressing effect on Jean who, when she takes it into her head to buy something, wants it yesterday. However, on the following Monday evening I returned home from work to find Jean, Stephen and Edie standing on the lawn beside a largish cage full of scrambling puppies. The cage was about three feet square and three feet high, made of stout steel rods with a one inch mesh. The whole thing was painted green and must have cost a fortune.

"How much?" I enquired.

"Smashing isn't it?" replied Jean, "exactly what we wanted. I found it in a shop just down the road, would you believe?"

"You haven't answered the question," I reminded her. Jean's face took on that set expression which I always think is peculiar to the female sex when they don't want to be questioned too closely.

"I'm paying for it, dear, and I know how much it was, so you need not worry… need you?" she added menacingly.

"Er… well… no. If you put it like that, I suppose not," I answered staring at the frame and in my mind's eye seeing it filled with beautifully rotting compost instead of Yorkie puppies. She must have read my thoughts because I was then informed that… 'No, I was not being made a present of it after the pups had gone because, hopefully, (here glancing dotingly at Charlie who was doing her best to jam her head into the mesh) there would be other litters to follow, wouldn't there Charlie?'

I never found out how much that cage cost and I haven't got a compost maker to this day. I don't feel too bad about it though, as my pal John and I have taken to pinching leaf mould from the local woods which is less money, a damn sight cheaper and more in keeping with the way things are conducted in our area. It is not, you understand, that I consort with criminals but, if something is lying about and nobody wants it, it seems sinful not to put it to good use. Besides, leaf mould is about two pounds a bag at the gardening stores.

I haven't mentioned John before and it was about this time that our friendship began to really develop. We had known him, his wife Pam and daughter Tracy for some years and, in the way that really firm friendships are made, we seemed to drift slowly together. John, who loves dogs, had a collie called Ben who adores everybody provided they don't try to get through the gate, and the Yorkie pups really fascinated both dog and master. We could see that John was having distinct pangs of anticipated ownership as he played with the puppies, and we wondered how long it would be before he came to the point. In the event he didn't. Not then anyway, but in a couple of years or so Ben was to have a Yorkie to keep him company.

There was no trouble finding the pups homes to go to, the world seemed to be beating a path to our door and we could have sold them three times over. This being our first litter of pedigree pups we had only a vague idea of the quality for either breeding or showing. We were not out to make a fortune for, as I have explained earlier, it is just not possible to make any real profit if all the various fees are paid to veterinary surgeons and the kennel club and the puppies are given the best care possible. In fact we sold, for a small amount, one of the small dogs as a pet which later turned out to be worth a few hundred pounds or more. The new owners loved the little chap and have consistently refused increasing offers for him, but it goes to show that it pays to find out all you can about the breed and just what to look for, both in the pedigree and in the puppies.

Jean, being the mathematical brain of the family, worked out that we had just about covered the cost of having the litter. Whether or not this included the cage, I can't say.

Charlie stayed, of course, and I was surprised that there was no resentment on Fred's part. In fact, she seemed quite pleased to have the little bitch around, and she set about bringing up her daughter in what was a most admirable way.

Fred can be most warlike and, had she been human, I feel that her ancestry would have owed more to Atilla the Hun than St. Francis of Assisi; so I suppose that it was only natural that as soon as Charlie was big enough, the fighting lessons began. These seemed to consist of much snarling and grabbing hold of back legs and, as Charlie grew older, a general free for all developed, Stephen occasionally joining in and getting nipped for interfering.

Winter came on and house training had been introduced for the pup but, much to Jean's disgust, Charlie just didn't seem to catch on at all. Life was too eventful and exciting to worry about minor details like lavatory arrangements and, although Charlie usually restricted her nightly activities to paper on the kitchen floor, the situation was obviously unsatisfactory to everybody, except Charlie of course; she didn't give a damn.

Another round of consultations with friends and breeders followed, and various gems of advice were imparted on the subject of how to teach our little dumb friend not to foul up carpets and kitchen floors. These pieces of information ranged from a rather elaborate system of love, care and tenderness which involved carrying the offender gently to the appointed place in the garden at the same time each day and gently crooning instructions into the dog's ear; to a swift kick up the backside which, or so the theory went, would at best give the animal a rough indication as to the area in which action was required or, at worst, project the offending material so far back into the dog that the problem did not present itself again for some little time.

I must confess that I had some sneaking regard for the second theory because, as I generally got up first in the mornings, the job of cleaning up nearly always fell my way. Naturally, Jean said I was a misguided bully and decided to try some of the other ideas, beginning with the love and kindness treatment.

In a week Charlie had reduced Jean to the level of a nervous wreck and Steve and me to laughter which sometimes bordered on hysteria. With gentle but firm hands Jean would carry Charlie to the appointed place and gently encourage her with choice phrases such as, 'who wants to do a little pile then?' or, alternatively, 'now Charlie let's have B.M.'. The latter remark induced mild convulsions in Steve and me; in Steve because I had told him about the last B.M. episode, even if he could not quite remember it himself; and in me because I had wild visions of Jean and Charlie doing a duet on the back lawn. Throughout the whole performance Charlie kept wagging her little tail and trying to lick Jean and was obviously very keen to oblige all and sundry in helping to solve the problem. The only drawback was that she had a distinctly cloudy idea of what the problem was. This performance usually lasted about ten minutes, after which Jean would stalk disgustedly into the kitchen, closely followed by an eager faced Charlie who promptly defecated on the floor. Occasionally, Charlie would follow this performance with a quick pee by way of an encore, which further fuelled the frustrated fury that was slowly boiling up inside Jean.

There were vague mutterings about dog psychologists from Jean as she sat on the sofa one day, her long legs curled beneath her and her brow furrowed as she attempted to solve a problem which was slowly turning the kitchen into something resembling a midden. Charlie usually sat watching her, trying to be helpful in her own way with an occasional twitch of the tail.

Fred took no interest in the proceedings and generally stood watching with Steve and me as Jean manfully, or womanfully, struggled to persuade Charlie that leaving piles in the house was antisocial.

And then, one evening when we were getting ready for bed, Charlie began scratching at the kitchen door. Jean could barely control her excitement.

"She wants to go out. She wants to go out." Fred and I (Stephen was in bed) followed Jean to the door and, sure enough, there was Charlie begging to be let out. Jean opened the door and Charlie hopped over the sill and trotted away into the darkness in the direction of the place where Jean had spent so much time trying to explain what was required of her. Five minutes passed and then Charlie reappeared, wagged her tail and jumped over the step into the kitchen.

"There!" yelled Jean delightedly. "We've cracked it... good old Charlie."

Everyone, including Fred, became quite excited and Charlie joined in eagerly, expressing herself by doing another pile on the kitchen floor.

There are few more depressing sights in this world than the face of a beaten woman. I cleaned up as Jean went dejectedly off to bed and, as Fred and Charlie bedded themselves down for the night in their basket, I followed her upstairs.

"It's just not fair," she cried. "Why is she such a mucky little pig? She's marvellous otherwise."

"I dunno, love," I replied, half in sadness, half in amusement. "Let's see what happens in the morning."

What did happen in the morning was absolutely nothing. The kitchen was as clean as a whistle. I congratulated Charlie on her comparative cleanliness and, as I opened the kitchen door, was surprised to see her follow Fred into the garden. They trotted up the path to the place where Jean had laboured for so long and, crouching side by side, proceeded to attend to their bodily needs.

Apart from the odd accident that every dog has, Charlie has, to this day, been a model of cleanliness and, although I didn't say so at the time, I believe that it was Jean's kindness and perseverance that helped Charlie over a very difficult obstacle that fate had placed in her life… the kitchen doorstep.

13

Lessons in Life

Charlie grew strong and well and, by the time a year was out, was almost as big as Fred. It was obvious that she would never grace the show ring at Crufts, or any other show ring for that matter. She was too big anyway; her body was a little too long and the colouring around her feet was not quite right, or so the experts said. However, we were informed that she would probably make an ideal brood bitch, which made Jean's eyes light up as Fred was now firmly in retirement.

The two dogs became almost inseparable and Fred, if anything, seemed to grow younger as they chased each other around the house and garden or the local parks and fields. There was no question as to who was the boss although Charlie tried it on with Fred a time or two but, each time she got uppish, Fred put her firmly in her place.

Gradually we began to notice Charlie's personality emerging and some of her behaviour was a little eccentric to say the least. She became very loving and faithful to all of us, but occasionally her actions led us to believe that she was a bit round the bend.

In one corner of the garden is a small grass hillock. When the builders moved out and Jean and I moved in many years ago, the usual collection of broken bricks and builders' rubble was left strewn about in the area where the lawn would eventually be. At that time I had ideas of building a rockery and I piled all the rubble in a heap and covered it with topsoil so that the lawn sloped up into a gently rounded mound. For some reason, which I cannot now remember, I changed my mind about the rockery, grassed the lot over and the mound became what we now call 'The Hill'. It's called Charlie's Hill now, for reasons which I am about to explain.

Charlie seemed rather taken with the hill. She would sit, motionless on the top, staring at the red cliffs at the top of the lane. At first we wondered what she was looking at or for but, try as we might, we never saw anything unusual while Charlie kept vigil. Fred takes very little interest in the hill, there doesn't seem any magic in it for her, but Charlie sits there for hours at a stretch. Rain does not deter her from doing sentry go and at first sign of snow she will be guarding her hill from we know not what only that, whatever it is, it must come from the direction of the red cliffs because almost always she faces the same way. One day, she sat out in a blizzard for so long that Jean had to fetch her indoors before she froze to death. I've got a feeling that either Charlie is barmy or that she knows something we don't. Whatever it is, it's all to do with the red cliffs. A neighbour planted a willow tree in his garden and, as it grew, it partially obscured the view of the cliffs, but Charlie still sits there anyway.

She is also much given to dancing and walking on her back legs. No-one has ever taught her to do this; she has done it from the days when she could barely walk. A breeder friend of ours refers to her as the local dancing dog, but she reminds me of a famous character in a strip cartoon, although she doesn't lie on her back on top of her kennel. She would find this rather difficult as she hasn't got a kennel, so perhaps that's why she doesn't do it. The walking and dancing can go on for minutes at a time and its frequency shows no sign of decreasing with her advancing years.

So you see, we are blessed with a dog that spends quite a large part of her life either walking around upright or sitting guarding her hill from the menace of the red cliffs.

Jean says that all this odd behaviour stems from the time when I inadvertently clouted her on the head with my slipper. What had started out as a gentle tap became quite a hard smack as the slipper toe accelerated in a whiplike action. It didn't seem to do her any harm at the time, but Jean says I've rearranged all her brain cells so that she thinks she is a Bluebell Girl who has been drafted into the army by mistake and has to guard a strategic hill against the advancing red hordes from the East. I point out to Jean that the cliffs are north east of the house, but Jean says I loused up her sense of direction as well. So there... ... ... ! Our friend John thinks that Charlie takes after the rest of the family and that Fred is the sole island of sanity in the house. He argues that, unlike Fred, Charlie has lived with us from birth and he has a theory that insanity is contagious. All I can say is that it takes one to know one.

* * *

Although we had officially retired Fred, it seemed that no-one had bothered to tell her so, as her next season came round (she had missed the one after her last litter), we had to go through the door closing performance again. This time we were successful in keeping her apart from the local lovers, although she seemed to adopt a fatalistic attitude and despite her condition, accepted the situation with good grace, not trying too hard to get out.

"She's going through the change you know," said Jean nodding wisely.

"What change?" inquired Stephen. I laughed and Jean glared at us both.

"She's going to change into an Alsatian," I remarked facetiously.

"Don't be daft," replied Steve as he settled down to read a comic. After the short silence that followed, I grinned wickedly at Jean.

"That got you off the hook, love."

"Yes it did rather, didn't it?" she smiled.

It may have been a sign of her advancing years that Fred began to adopt a more tolerant attitude towards cats. She would, and indeed still will, chase them out of the garden but we get a distinct impression that she does not really want to catch up with them nowadays as, more often than not, she stops at the garden fence and contents herself with a few sharp barks to send them away. This is a much happier situation as, while I don't have cats in the garden, we don't have to make any embarrassing explanations to neighbours or alternatively, have Fred coming back home looking as though she has just started World War Three.

The one exception is the cat that Fred can never beat. She is a charming little cat called Katie who lives three doors away from us. The main reason that Fred has never been able to do anything about Katie's intrusion into the garden (and God knows, she has intruded over the years) is that she can never catch her. Besides being a pretty cat Katie has brains, and long ago she devised a method of getting on top of our coal bunker to sunbathe in the summer time, irrespective of whether Fred happened to be about. She works it this way. In the safety of her own gated garden she hops on to the fence, walks delicately along it to the next house, then along their fence and so on until she reaches our garden gate. The coal bunker is alongside the fence separating our house from the next, and she makes her way sure-footedly along to it in the same fashion, seemingly oblivious to the impotent snarling and leaping that is going on beneath her. The snarling and leaping comes from Charlie now as Fred has long given up hope of ever bringing Katie to battle.

The insult is somewhat compounded as, very

occasionally, this composed and elegant of cats will dangle a paw over the edge of the bunker and take a playful swipe at whichever dog happens to be near and not looking at the time. After her period of sun and relaxation she will return the same way, again in her unhurried fashion, to the accompaniment of more barking and jumping. A rather splendid animal really and while, as you may have gathered, I am not a cat person, I have a sneaking regard for Katie.

But Charlie never gives up and I don't think it will ever get through to her that Katie is not any ordinary run of the mill moggie. Perhaps it's all part of the Red Cliff Syndrome. She falls for it every time and is usually the one to get clobbered round the ear, Fred keeping her distance while Katy is sunbathing.

Fred would nip off sometimes on various errands as the mood took her, but her excursions became less frequent except when Jean occasionally had an attack of the morning temper. She would not take the risk of being involved in whatever variety of mudslinging happened to take place and made off at a good clip, provided of course that the back door was open and, with Steve around, that was always a distinct possibility.

About that time John had taken to bringing Ben down with him on his not infrequent visits, and the house seemed full of dogs for the first few minutes after their arrival, before everything settled down to comparative orderliness. Ben, I am convinced, had a great influence on Charlie in her early years; not as much as Fred's mother/daughter relationship but in a most unusual way. Lean and rangy, Ben must be the envy of everyone whoever joined a slimming club or merely just wanted to shed a few pounds. His eating habits would make a Japanese Sumo wrestler look like an ascetic. If it's edible Ben will eat it, usually in one gulp, and then come back for more. His insatiable appetite very often gets him into trouble but, as he has strong if slim shoulders, when it comes to chastisement he bounces back before long. A skilful if endearing thief, Ben can go through a house like a vacuum cleaner and, unlike smaller animals, is not hampered by the height of tables. Of course, when John or anyone else is around, he presents the usual pricked ears and doleful eyes in the presence of food, but once human backs are turned... Charlie watched carefully as Ben repeatedly got into trouble for either sneaking or snatching at food and she must have decided that the stern words and sharp smacks received from John were not worth it. It's no good tapping Ben and speaking softly, he takes that as a sign of approval. Therefore, as Charlie grew older, she developed a very ladylike attitude towards her eating habits which she certainly did not inherit from her mother.

Fred scrounges around like Ben but being unable, because of her size, to take anything unless it is on the floor, presents only a minor problem. If either Jean or I are working in the kitchen preparing food, Fred will immediately gobble up any scrap which may happen to fall to the floor, but this does not apply to Charlie. She will sit and look up pleading to be given the word to take the food, by which time Fred had usually nipped in first.

Charlie is always compensated for her good manners and, in the end, generally gets the better of the deal much, I imagine, to Fred's disgust. But in later life this gentleness of Charlie has worked to her benefit.

One winter's night Steve and I sat round the fire roasting chestnuts on an old fashioned toasting fork in the glowing coals. When we had accumulated a small pile of the cooling shelled nuts, the dogs pricked up their ears as that glorious smell spread around the room and jumped down from Jean's lap in anticipation. Jean does not share their enthusiasm as she doesn't like roasted chestnuts, but then we all have our problems.

"Tell you what, Dad," said Steve, eyeing the dogs. "We'll eat this lot and they can have some of the next roasting, seeing as we have a bagful."

Jean may not like chestnuts but she certainly isn't stingy when it comes to buying them.

I nodded. "Good thinking, Carruthers."

"Who's Carruthers?" Steve enquired.

"Never mind," I replied, "dig in."

We dug in and, as I leaned back in my chair, feet crossed before the roaring blaze, I reflected on the contentment that I have been lucky enough to experience in my family life. I looked at Jean, curled up on the sofa deep in a book, and at Steve stuffing away his roast chestnuts. My arm had fallen over the arm of the chair, a chestnut between thumb and index finger and, as I raised hand to mouth, saw that I was holding nothing. I hadn't even felt it go but there was Charlie, soft of mouth, happily munching away on the hearthrug. Fred was absolutely wild with jealousy and tried to take away Charlie's treat, but I gently pushed her away with my foot. After all, in an ideal world, virtue coupled with expertise must certainly have its own reward.

14

Food, Glorious Food

In the springtime of the following year Jean was bitten by the party bug. Normally, I don't mind the odd party here or there as I can fall over and make a fool of myself with the best of them and, unless they are held in your own home, parties are generally free – if you discount the obligatory bottle of booze that is carted along to help replenish the stocks of whoever has been foolish enough to hold the party in the first place.

However, after Jean had told me about the invitation, I bridled somewhat when I found out that it didn't apply to me. This one was an 'all girls' party' and, although men were not strictly barred, they were certainly not encouraged to attend. Further enquiries about this gathering brought forth a reluctant admission from Jean that this type of 'party' involved buying something but, I was told, that was not really the important part which was that the ladies of the neighbourhood had a chance to get together for a cup of tea and chew over the fat about this and that. Presumably, 'this and that 'included the respective husbands who were absent. I could quite see that the presence of even one bloke would put the fat in the fire, so to speak, so I concentrated on the buying bit.

Getting a true idea of this was extremely difficult but, piece by piece, the picture became clear. It seemed that a friend of a friend, who had a friend, sold some kind of container which was not available in the shops. This philanthropic lady was going around to people's houses loaded with the junk and persuading a gang of gullible women to fill their homes with piles of plastic boxes that they didn't want. Jean should know… she used to sell the stuff for a short time shortly after Stephen was born. She did it, partly to get out of the house while I did the babysitting, but mostly for the small amount of money she made which came in very handy. We were rather skint at the time as a new house, new furniture, a new baby and a car can prove rather expensive when they all come at the same time.

Things have changed slightly for the better for us now, and the argument is more likely to be about which of us paid for the last case of wine, but it does no harm to remind oneself of earlier struggles. When we grumble about not being able to afford this or that, Jean and I think of those years and the memories bring us down with a bump and make us rather ashamed of ourselves for complaining.

I had visions of a struggling young mother desperately trying to sell enough to pay for the baby's next feed (I'm a sentimental twit and a soft touch for the truly unfortunate). So I gave Jean my blessing and she trotted off to the 'Party'. A couple of hours later she returned with armfuls of the awful stuff to add to the pile we already had left over from years ago. With a beaming smile of having done your good deed for the day (yes, the lady had been a young mother), Jean informed me that next week Edie was having a party and all were invited. It wasn't plastic this time but ladies' slips, bras, pants and things and the men were definitely not invited to this one.

"Then," she continued, "the following week we are having a party here."

"Oh Lor!" I groaned, "What's yours for then, biscuit boxes or knickers?"

"Knickers!" replied Jean, neatly killing two birds with one stone.

* * *

The parties came and went in a flurry and slowly died away but, out of the few weeks of frenzied activity (not to mention the high level financial transactions), there emerged a friendship that was to prove strong and true. At one of the parties Jean met a lady named Joan. Looking back over the years, it is difficult to imagine what life was like without Joan, her amiable husband Jack and their six year old blonde bombshell of a daughter called Victoria. Joan has that happy knack that we wish was common to all our friends. She is helpful, but never intrusive. The sort of person that everyone

122

would like for a mother; she can cope with everything from a cut finger to an earthquake. Nothing seems to deter her from her course, difficulties being something to be met and overcome, generally with a broad smile upon her face.

Steve, Fred and Charlie worship her and she adores them, particularly Charlie. The three of them spend a lot of time at Joan's home which is nearby and as Steve passes the house on his way to school in the morning, he calls in to pick up Victoria and, when Jean and I are both out for the day at our respective occupations, to leave the dogs to chase and run around her garden or sleep before the fire as the mood takes them. She spoils them terribly and, although I know that she genuinely tries to ignore their pleas for titbits, I also know that they can twist her around their tiny paws.

The teacher and the housewife have a lot in common, most of which proves beneficial to Jack and me because, while we are slogging away in our gardens, Jean and Joan are busy in the late summer and autumn making jam and raspberry and blackberry vinegar, bottling and storing all the good things to see us through the winter months. Like most children, Steve and Victoria love homemade jam and I don't think either of our families has bought a jar of industrially produced jam for years. This statement is not strictly true as one year Jean fell for an advertising campaign on television and decided to test the claims of the manufacturer of a well known brand, whose main claim to fame was that the lid closed with a resounding thud. It was late spring and she had committed the unforgivable sin of running out of the homemade strawberry so, one teatime, brand X was placed before Stephen.

"I'm not eating that," he stated.

"Why not?" glowered Jean.

"It's got a label on with a picture. Proper jam just says STRAW 1976."

Under pressure from his mother Steve eventually sampled the product as he is not by nature a disobedient boy, but he just about reduced Jean to a giggling heap with the faces he pulled. We have never run out of jam since.

Fred and Charlie must have liked the sort of food Joan served because, when they were not on their daily visits in school term time, they took to sloping off up the lane to Joan's in search of whatever she was prepared to give them. They began to grow rather fat and we had to impose a rather strict dietary regime which did wonders for their shape and general fitness. Everybody cooperated and within a fortnight they were fighting fit again.

Then, Fred slowly started to put on weight again, thickening out round the middle. We watched her closely but couldn't find out where the extra food was coming from. It wasn't from Joan and it wasn't from us. Charlie remained unaffected and at one stage we thought that the additional weight was due to Fred's age. The weeks went by and she got fatter and fatter. Jean had already cut down the amount of food she ate at home but it seemed to make no difference. Fred's belly bulged like a brewer's goitre as she belched and hiccupped her way round the house and garden.

And then, one Sunday, we found out Fred's secret.

Behind the house is a small courtyard. Along one side are seven garages, one for each of the houses which form our small block. The back gardens of three of the houses are on the opposite side of the yard. On this particular Sunday Jean had taken eggs to Jaqi and Adrian who live in the house furthest away from us. Jaqi and Jean stood gossiping on the doorstep when Jean heard a familiar sound. Very faintly came the tink-tink-tink of a dog's metal identification disc tapping on a plate. Both Fred and Charlie wear the tags bearing our name and address – not their own name. The round discs always hang below their chins and when they feed the discs tap on the side of their bowls making a metallic ringing sound.

That was the sound that Jean heard now and that meant only one thing – food. Quite recently Jaqi had acquired a new next door neighbour; a lady who lived alone and kept very much to herself. She was always polite and friendly and we didn't see a lot of her but Fred obviously did. Peering over the fence Jean saw our tubby terrier tucking into an oversize dinner plate full of roast beef, potatoes, Brussels' sprouts, carrots and, rather appropriately, Yorkshire pudding, all covered in rich gravy. Sybil, for that was the lady's name, came to her open back door, beamed at the staring faces of Jean and Jaqi and nodded at Fred.

"Just giving her a little snack," she smiled. Jean was speechless; there was enough to feed an army. Diplomacy is not one of Jean's strong points. Coming from Yorkshire, she is very likely to call a spade a bloody shovel but this time she handled what was a tricky situation with flair and imagination. At least that was what she said afterwards.

While thanking Sybil for her kindness towards a small dumb animal, she gently stressed that Yorkshire terriers were supposed to look like Yorkshire terriers and not like miniature hairy pigs. Sybil smiled and nodded and said she understood but remarked that it was very difficult to remember good advice when faced with the pleading eyes, or in Fred's case, eye, of an obviously undernourished animal. Normally, this last remark would have brought forth a stern lecture from Jean on the food intake required to maintain a happy and healthy dog but, as this was diplomacy day, she contented herself with the mildest of rebukes and managed to extract a promise from Sybil not to continue the banquets which had obviously been going on for some weeks.

Joan giggled when she heard the story and tried to keep a straight face. I think that the idea of Jean struggling to be diplomatic amused her but at least the problem was solved, or at least we thought so at the time.

Fred went on 'iron rations' and gradually assumed a shape more befitting a Yorkie and after a short time we re-introduced her normal diet. Throughout this period Charlie remained unaffected. It has always puzzled me why she didn't follow Fred to the feeding orgies at Sybil's house as she follows her nearly everywhere else. But she never did. Sybil would have almost certainly fed them both, but Charlie seemed content to sit on her hill and wait for her share of 'home cooking'.

Like all good guerrilla fighters Sybil bided her time before striking again. The weeks went by and then Fred again started to swell. This time we were forewarned and a family conference took place. Everyone agreed, including John who had been roped in and had suggested sending Ben in Fred's place, that an out an out confrontation with fixed bayonets etc. was out of the question. Apart from the fact that Sybil objects to Steve trying to emulate Kevin Keegan (a footballer of no little renown) outside her back door on Sunday afternoons, we all get on pretty well in the court. All in all, we are a happy little band compared to most neighbours, apart from minor tiffs, usually about the kids, and it is a situation we all wish to preserve.

Around our houses we have what is euphemistically termed 'ranch fencing' and it is easy for the dogs to hop over the bottom plank and out into the court, but drastic situations demand drastic measures.

"We'll net it," said Jean. "You know that strong metal mesh. Net the bottom two planks of the fence and they can't get through." She smiled hugely at John and me.

"I suppose that 'we' means you and me," said John as he crossed his long legs and glanced at me.

"Looks like it, mate," I replied, "if you're willing to help."

"I'd better," he said shortly. "Anything involving a hammer and you're quite likely to break your thumb."

So we sweated and netted, hammering staples into

the woodwork to hold the strong mesh that Jean had acquired. I use the word 'acquired' advisedly, as she was dropping into the local habits and we didn't enquire too closely as to how and where the wire mesh had come into her possession. I think it fell off the back of the proverbial lorry.

I don't really know if the wire mesh worked or not, but Fred remained slim and fit. Of course, they have found a way out of the garden again, but Fred does not get too fat anymore and Charlie is a bit of a stay at home anyway. Steve is still not too popular with Sybil, as he rehearses on the court for the next World Cup and perhaps that has some bearing on Fred, who thinks Steve is the fairy on top of the Christmas tree.

I can't be sure, but I think I caught a glimpse of a congealed plate of roast beef and Yorkshire pud beside a back door as I went to the garage one Sunday afternoon.

15

A Close Shave

The party the previous night had gone on longer than anyone had intended. It had started out with dinner for ourselves and four friends (no plastic boxes or ladies' underwear buying) and, as we sat around the fire talking, Saturday had turned into Sunday and it was about three o'clock in the morning before things broke up and our guests left. Jean and I tidied up the house, made a cup of tea and smoked a final cigarette before tumbling into bed around four o'clock.

Stephen, of course, had been asleep for hours. After having dinner he had been allowed to stay up for an extra hour and by nine thirty was tucked up in bed, his eyelids already dropping as he said his prayers. At seven thirty in the morning Stephen decided to have some recorder practice. He had been learning to play the instrument at school with some coaching from Jean, who is quite an accomplished player, and he had recently found out that it was not just 'school music' that could be played on recorders. Selections from 'Top of the Pops' had come in for some stick in the last week or two, but at half past seven in the morning his enthusiasm for the Top Twenty was not shared by Jean.

I was in that dreamy state of semi-wakefulness as the shrilling notes of the latest chartbuster broke the stillness of that early Sunday morning. The dreamy state lasted all of ten seconds before I was out of bed and dashing into Stephen's room to snatch the offending instrument away from my indignant son, who informed me that I was not being fair because he had just mastered a particularly tricky piece. He received a stern lecture on recorders and the playing thereof at unseemly and unsocial hours, but it was too late. From our bedroom came the grumbling and heaving sounds that usually are the beginning of loud protests from a wife being robbed of her beauty sleep. Stephen immediately apologised and said he thought it was later than it actually was and anyway his watch had stopped. But the damage was done.

Outraged howls of protest rang through the house as Jean demanded to know why we didn't get the Brighouse and Rastrick Brass Band in as well and then we could wake up the whole neighbourhood and give everybody a tune. Stephen recognised the storm warning signs immediately and began to creep around like a mouse.

"It's a bit late for that, mate," I observed as I returned to two bleary eyes set in a frowning face peeping over the bedclothes.

"It's all right, love," I began, "he didn't know the time, thought it was much later. Anyway," I continued,

"I'm awake now, so I'll go downstairs and cook breakfast while you have a doze."

Jean turned over still grumbling and muttering death threats to all and sundry and particularly Stephen, while he and I dressed and went downstairs to put the kettle on and fry bacon and eggs. I let the dogs go out of the kitchen door, wincing as they whooped and barked, racing round the garden on what looked very much like the beginning of a beautiful autumn day. Stephen was still pussyfooting around, so I sent him off to fetch the Sunday papers while I set to in the kitchen. The dogs came back indoors, panting and covered in dew where they had been rolling on the lawn and, seeing the frying pan in my hand, sat down expectantly, tails wagging. Bacon is a treat for them on Sundays. They have just a small piece each but the smell of it in the pan makes them drool and shiver in anticipation. Steve returned with the papers and I decided to take Jean's breakfast up to the bedroom but, as I prepared the tray, loud thumping noises came from upstairs as the lady clumped into the bathroom.

It's best to say very little when such a situation develops at home. Steve was already looking for cover after a quick glance at the ceiling.

"Oh heck," he said. "It's getting up." He glanced sideways at me. "Do you think she'll be mad?"

After more clumping and banging, interspersed with ominous silences, came the sound of heavy footsteps on the stairs. The footsteps stopped abruptly and were followed by several loud bangs, a crash and a lot of rather doubtful language. The swearing did much to reassure me that Jean was not hurt too badly and I hurried into the hall to see an irate wife rubbing her knees and again threatening death to the person or persons unknown who had left a pair of shoes in the middle of the hall. The fact that the shoes were her own seemed to have little to do with the situation and I was not inclined to press the point as Jean staggered into the living room like a crippled battleship with all guns firing.

Stephen politely inquired if 'mummy was alright' and was rewarded with a venomous glare. Charlie hid under the stairs and of Fred there was no sign. As Jean's temperature reduced to a slow simmer we sat down to breakfast. Charlie poked a tentative nose round the kitchen door, the smell of bacon overriding her fears. Jean's temper rapidly improved as the bacon and eggs went down (it always does) and presently things returned to near normal, Jean even smiling at Steve. Not a very big smile to be sure, more a grimace really, but the situation was on the mend.

Charlie turned up for her bacon but there was no Fred. We then realised that Steve had done his trick with the garden gate when he returned with the papers and, when the fireworks had started, Fred had decided that she wanted no part of it, perhaps believing the invective to be directed at her, and she had well and truly hopped it.

We searched the garden and court and Jean, now anxious and contrite, made herself really popular by picking up the telephone and ringing nearby friends who Fred visited from time to time to see if she had turned up. After ten minutes of searching and telephoning we still had no idea where she was. She had gone off on her own before but this time some instinct seemed to drive Jean to find her.

"I'll go and see Edie, she's always up early, perhaps she'll help," said Jean anxiously as she put on a sweater. "She will help... I'm sure she will... I'll get Joan as well." I looked at the clock, it was nine o'clock on a beautiful autumn Sunday, the early morning had kept its promise. Then the front doorbell rang.

They stood at the front door looking like an overworked and rather scruffy pop group. Long hair, fringed leather jackets and denims. Four of them. Parked across the street was a large beaten up van, engine still running.

"We couldn't miss it mister, it ran straight under the van. We got the address off the dog tag. Honest mister, we didn't stand a chance." Cradled in the arms of a leather jacket was Fred. A twisted and smashed up Fred that bore hardly any resemblance to the perky Yorkie that had run away such a short time ago. I looked at her and then at the faces of the four young men. The compassion, concern and understanding that I saw there almost moved me to the tears that I could see welling in the eyes of the boy who held Fred so gently in his arms. I didn't know how to thank them for bringing her home. 'Thank you' didn't seem enough but I knew that to offer anything but that would have been an insult to them. As carefully as I could, I took Fred from the boy.

"You've been great, fellas, thank you."

"S'alright, mister," said one. "We're ever so sorry but she just… "

I cut them short, "It wasn't your fault and thank you again for bringing her home, many wouldn't have bothered."

"Yeah, well, er… we'd best be going then."

"Yeah, you've got enough to do now, mister, without us hanging around," said another as they moved off down the path.

I've never seen them since. If I did I'd buy each of them the biggest drink they could manage. In fact, they could all get stoned and I wouldn't quibble about the bill. If they were a pop group, I hope they are at the top of the hit parade. They are certainly at the top of mine.

I carried Fred into the house calling for Steve to hurry and find Jean. His eyes filled up as he saw what was left of Fred and he dashed off shouting for his mother. As I looked at Fred again the one good eye looked back and blinked… at least she was still alive.

At times Jean may dither, occasionally she panics, but when a real crisis arises she swings into action with all the assurance of an old midwife delivering her hundredth baby. She rang the vet and, not waiting for him to visit, laid Fred on a blanket, put her on the back seat of the car and was off to his surgery. Sunday mornings must be an awkward time for veterinary surgeons but we had no difficulties – he told us to bring her round at once.

Steve and I stayed at home, tidying up and generally putting the house to rights. Charlie could not, for the life of her, understand what was happening. Although by now an almost fully grown dog, she had never been separated from Fred and didn't know what had happened to her or why she had been suddenly taken away in Jean's arms. As Jean was making the phone call and I was fussing over Fred, Charlie came to sniff at her mother and immediately realised something was wrong when Fred just lay still, staring piteously up at me. Charlie retired to her basket and, chin on paws, silently watched as Steve and I washed up the breakfast plates and dishes.

Time dragged on as I tried to take an interest in the newspapers but, after reading a few lines, I threw them aside and began to prowl aimlessly around the house as we waited to hear from Jean. We didn't have to wait long. Within an hour Jean was back, without Fred.

"She's got a broken pelvis and the ligaments are torn and God knows what else," Jean informed us. "The vet's keeping her for twenty four hours to see what develops, but he says there is not a lot he can do. She's getting on in years but he says she may have a chance if no complications set in. It's just a case of wait and see," she ended mournfully. So we waited, but saw very little that Sunday. Jean telephoned the surgery again in the afternoon but there was no change in Fred's condition, which may or may not have been a good sign. We just didn't know. Charlie caught the mood of general quietness that had fallen over the house and was no longer her boisterous self. Altogether a very glum day indeed, I reflected, as we went to bed. That night

Stephen included Fred in his prayers and, I must confess, I did in mine.

Jean brought her home on the Monday evening, together with a list of instructions from the vet. Time alone would heal her, if at all, but at best she would, in all probability, be permanently crippled, barring miracles. At worst, if any complications did set in, she would have to be put down. We should know after ten days as, after that period, the vet said, she should be trying to walk again. Meanwhile she had to be kept warm and quiet.

Another cardboard box lined with the fleecy whelping blanket came into play, placed beside the fire. A friend, who runs an upholstery business, hearing of her plight, provided a covered foam cushion fitted to the size of the box. The blanket lay on top of the cushion so we felt we had made her as comfortable as we could.

Fred ate little or nothing for the first few days but she lapped at the milk and honey which Jean gave her. Each night and morning we carried her into the garden and held her while she rid herself of whatever waste products she had managed to accumulate from her meagre diet.

During those days Fred lay very still, hardly moving at all, spending most of her time seeming to be asleep. Every evening Charlie came and lay down beside Fred's box as if keeping guard. It seemed that the hill would have to look after itself for a while.

After a fortnight she showed no signs of improvement although her appetite had improved a little. I telephoned the vet and gave him a progress report and, at the same time, asked him what he thought her chances of survival were.

"Well," he replied slowly, "if she was really improving she should at least have tried to walk, are you sure there are no signs of movement?" I told him, sadly, that she had hardly moved since the day Jean brought her home.

"Well, give her two or three more days and then, if nothing happens, bring her down to the surgery. She's got a fifty – fifty chance of making it. Don't give up hope yet." But Fred didn't move a muscle and two days later she was still motionless in her box beside the fire.

The following day I was off work and, after Jean and Stephen had gone off to school, I walked Charlie up to Joan and Jack's house for the day. Joan had kept an eye on Fred while Jean and I were out during the daytime and we fell to discussing the possibilities of Fred's recovery. Joan was of the same mind as the vet, that we should not give up hope and, while I fervently agreed, I added that, as she had not moved at all, the signs were hardly encouraging.

"Never mind," said Joan as she bustled about her kitchen. "Hope springs eternal, that's what they say isn't it?"

"Yes, Joan," I smiled, "that's what they say."

"Well then," she said briskly, "why don't you nip off to the club for a game of snooker or whatever it is you do down there, and stop worrying?" So I nipped off to the club for a game of snooker – in fact several games of snooker and I didn't return home until the early afternoon.

It was beginning to turn cold and I was glad that I had lit a fire that morning. I could see the red glow through the window as I walked to the back door. I also saw something else which was such a familiar sight that it didn't register with me until I was in the house. For there, lying on the hearthrug, was Fred, her eyes closed. As she heard me come into the room she opened her one eye, looked at me and wagged her tail.

Gleefully I threw the empty box to the other end of the room and, grinning like an idiot, sat down to put on my slippers.

16

Getting Better

With a twisted spine and one back leg held high against her body, Fred limped and struggled her way around the house. It was pitiful to see her and we had to restrain ourselves from trying to help too much. Jean had been assured by our veterinary surgeon, who seemed as relieved as we were to hear of her progress, that Fred knew best and that we should let her make her own way in her own time. But sometimes it was very difficult as we watched her stagger painfully from her box to lie before the fire. We still, of course, helped her to get out of the house and back again but the rest of the time she limped along at a snail's pace. One rather amusing thing to come out of the whole affair was the sudden acquisition of rather less ferocious feeding habits. For the first and only time in her life, Fred ate daintily. She seemed to prefer still to eat by Charlie's side in the kitchen and, as her appetite slowly improved, so the time taken from hearthrug to kitchen at feeding time decreased.

Charlie was wonderful. She seemed to suddenly understand what was required of her and became the perfect dutiful daughter. She waited patiently for Fred at mealtimes and afterwards would escort her back to the warmth of the fire where she would clean Fred's face and damaged eye carefully. This was followed by much gentle nose pushing and snuffling all around, as she assured herself that her mother was as comfortable as could be expected. Only then would she settle down by Fred's side usually, during those early days after the accident, for the rest of the evening.

For the most part Fred was content to spend her time asleep but, as the weeks went slowly by, her attempts to walk became more frequent and, although the back leg remained drawn up high against her body, her back began to straighten from the almost 90 degree curve with which the accident had left her. However, we were becoming resigned to the fact that she would probably be crippled for the rest of her life but, provided she was in no pain, we were more than happy that she had survived such a terrible accident, even if recovery was only partial. But we had not fully reckoned with the sheer guts and determination of our little dog. John once remarked to me that it was a good job Yorkies were not the size of Great Danes or someone would have a proper handful. I couldn't agree with him more. Fred showed enough heart and courage to keep a pride of lions in business as she stubbornly refused to be beaten. We could almost hear her cursing and swearing as she hauled herself around, scorning help unless it was absolutely necessary. As her back straightened, albeit painfully slowly, she would keep trying to get over the high storm step and out of the kitchen door. Jean, Steve or I, whoever happened to be about, would give her a lift and she would stagger off into the garden.

Then one day, she got herself a little too far over the step and fell in a heap on to the concrete path. Jean, who had been about to help, rushed to comfort her, but she slowly picked herself up and glared at Jean. Then we understood... this was victory. She had bloody well got out on her own and the next thing was to bloody well get back in again. It took her a month, a month of struggling in, what must have been, utter frustration and fatigue. The ever straightening back must have helped, but the leg was still useless. Twice she almost made it, but each time fell back exhausted in impotent rage, rumbling and muttering to herself.

Then one day she tried again, the three good legs fighting and scrambling for purchase. The front legs were doing fine but the single back leg seemed so weak as she fought and swore her way slowly, ever so slowly, over the step. Steve anxiously rushed to help but was stopped by a quiet word from Jean. Drawing on strength, from God knows where, she at last got the bad leg on to the high step and half fell, half walked into the kitchen.

Everybody cheered and clapped and, amid an abundance of 'well done's' and 'good old Fred's', we all congratulated her. Charlie joined in with a few well chosen barks and Fred seemed very pleased too, wagging her tail furiously as Charlie and Stephen danced around her.

Another milestone in Fred's journey to recovery had been passed. We all had a little party that night. We're a very happy house really.

* * *

Fred gradually grew better in health and temper as the improvement continued. Getting about involved less sweat and muted snarling and, now that the kitchen doorstep had been mastered, life must have been more pleasant for her as she could wander around the house and garden almost at will. She never attempted to leave the garden and, although Jean sometimes sighed as she watched the awkward gait, we were all glad that she was more or less mobile again. With her appetite now fully restored, Fred abandoned her delicate nibbling and pitched in at mealtimes with her previous no nonsense approach. Charlie even enticed her into a mock fight now and again and the pair rolled around on the lawn playfully snarling and wrestling. During the evenings Jean lifted Fred onto her lap and gently massaged the 'rear offside', as she put it. But while the leg was not wasted, it stubbornly refused to function properly. A great deal of attention was paid to that leg and Fred received much cosseting and stroking as Jean laboured away.

"If only she could get it going again she would be as good as new," remarked Jean one evening. "Her back is straight enough now and, well it's such a shame, but I knew we couldn't hope for too much, still, I'll keep trying."

Some days later I observed Fred gently strolling round the garden. It was a weekday morning, I was having a day off and Jean and Stephen had not long left for their respective schools. It must have been a Friday as, when my day off falls on a Friday, it is one of my duties to pay the milkman and I remember that that was what I had just done as I glanced through the window. 'Madam', as Jean sometimes refers to her, was calmly strolling around taking the morning air and pausing occasionally for the odd sniff here and there. Nothing unusual in that, except that her morning constitutional involved the use of ALL FOUR LEGS! I watched, fascinated, as she trotted up to Charlie who, of course, was on hill duty. They sat for a while staring at the cliffs and then Fred turned and lolloped down the gentle slope, all four legs still going. I went outside and called her. Her head flicked round and, as she saw me, one back leg flew up to her body like a rocket. She hobbled towards me on three legs.

You can't argue with a dog. I knew what I had seen, but for the rest of the morning the leg stayed up. I even fell to sneaking up on her, but she must have heard me coming and I just could not catch her out.

Jean and Steve didn't really believe me when they came home from school and I recounted the events of the morning.

"Yes, dear," said Jean politely. (She can be infuriating

143

at times). Steve didn't even bother being polite. He looked sideways at me and went out to play. We sat down to a drink before dinner and Fred hobbled in (still on three legs) to be cosseted by Jean. Inquiries were made about 'Fred's poorly leg' as I grew more agitated.

"There's nothing wrong with her bloody leg," I howled. "She's been walking perfectly normally... it's when she's being watched..." I rambled on.

"I suppose she pulls her leg up when she's being watched, does she?" inquired Jean mildly. "And then, when she thinks nobody is looking, she walks normally?"

"Yes, yes, that's it," I was getting a little wild now

"Ah, yes... I've got kids in my class like that... see things that aren't there and so on... lay off the beer for a bit, love, keep taking the tablets and you should be fine."

"I'm telling you it's true, she's been conning us." I calmed down. "Look love... it's as true as I sit here. I know what I saw, and she's back on all four legs," I said, glaring at Fred as she stood on three.

"Honest?" asked Jean.

"Honest," I replied.

But Fred still kept walking about on three legs and my credibility took quite a bashing over the next three days. I began to develop fiendish plots to expose Fred and vindicate myself, but each time she was a jump ahead. She must have ears like a lynx. Three days later I caught her again, but this time I said nothing to Jean and Steve. I said plenty to Fred however, and I reckon she must have taken pity on me because a day or two later she condescended to demonstrate, albeit hesitantly, the use of all four legs to the assembled family. Nothing spectacular, she just trotted up to Jean. Jean and Stephen were delighted and I adopted that languid air, so beloved of those who are 'always proved right in the end'. It did me no good, however, as I was completely ignored. Fred was the centre of attention as more congratulations were showered upon her and I was accused of being peevish and unchristian because I didn't join in.

Charlie jumped up on my lap and tried to clean my face. Now that Fred was well again she would have to find a new patient to nurse. Nobody even made reference to my claims of the previous week. Even when I tried to point out that Fred was probably unwilling to demonstrate her return to health for fear of missing the nightly fussing from Jean, my opinions were derided. It's a hard life being right. Of course it's Charlie's fault really. She was witness to the whole event and she might have dropped a word in Jean's ear. Just to put the matter straight, I mean.

Who said, 'If only they could talk'? Mind you, perhaps it's a good job they can't. Fred learnt an awful lot of new words from me that week.

17

Another Generation

Although Fred had occupied most of the attention of ourselves and our friends for the past few months, Charlie had been by no means neglected and, as her second season approached, I noticed that John in particular was taking a more than passing interest in her welfare. A quiet man by nature, he is not given to being over-demonstrative but his inquiries, coupled with frequent surreptitious inspections of Charlie's rear end, led me to believe that, should Charlie present us with a litter, we would have no trouble finding a home for at least one little dog.

Trying to catch him by surprise one night, over a quiet pint in the Chequers, I suddenly sprung what I thought was guaranteed to throw him off balance.

"What sort do you fancy, then?" I asked. We had been discussing cricket and I was sure that a sudden question that had nothing to do with the current subject would at least bring an inquiry as to what the hell I was talking about. John slowly put down his glass of beer and his hazel eyes slitted as he gazed at the wall behind me for a few seconds.

"A bitch, I think," he said shortly, picking up the glass and draining it. "It's your shout," he said nodding at Janet, behind the bar, to refill our glasses. Then he turned to me and grinned.

"How did you know… ?" I began.

"Great minds, my old son, great minds… mind you that's always supposing she has a bitch, or even a litter."

"I think Jean might have the matter in hand." I said quietly.

"No, no, son, it's Charlie who's got to get pregnant, it's a dog I want. I've got one daughter and that's enough."

"Who's pregnant?" interrupted Janet, putting freshly pulled pints on the bar.

"That's up to him," said John, cocking a thumb in my direction.

"No it isn't, Jan," I cut in, "it's up to Charlie."

"Charlie who?" inquired Janet, now intrigued.

"It's Jean's new fella," said John, his face straight as a die.

"Ooo… er, when did all this happen then?"

"It hasn't, yet," John informed her. "But we're negotiating, aren't we, Rog?"

"Yeah," I replied dolefully, and then John roared with laughter, beckoned Janet over and whispered in her ear.

"Aaaaah!" smiled Janet as John explained. "But why do you call her Charlie if she's a girl?"

"It's a long story, Jan," I sighed. "Be a good girl and fill these up again. It's his shout this time."

For her first litter, Charlie presented us with one large dog and a near catastrophe. The live pup was born without incident but a second larger dog presented itself the wrong way round and Jean had, once again, to charge off to the vet, this time with a dead puppy half in and half out of its mother, strangled by its own umbilical cord. To our utter astonishment Charlie didn't even bat an eyelid and, once the pup had been removed, showed no ill effects, getting down to the business of motherhood like a veteran. It must have been her youth but, after two days, she didn't even look as if she had had puppies, let alone such a traumatic time.

When she wasn't feeding or cleaning her remaining pup, she would play around setting up mock fights with Fred and generally behaving as though nothing unusual had happened. The only spot of bother arose when grandmother tried to babysit for her daughter. Fred didn't seem to understand that the puppy did not belong to her and one day when she tried to get into the cage, which had been left open by an oversight on somebody's part, Charlie, gentle loving Charlie, let her have it. We didn't know whether to laugh or cry. Defending her solitary puppy, Charlie tore into Fred with all the self righteousness of affronted motherhood.

Fred was too startled to fight back. No-one was hurt in the encounter and Fred retired in confusion to stare up at Jean as though pleading to know what she had done wrong. There was no repetition of the incident,

Charlie never again presuming to chastise her mother, but a precedent had been set which was thereafter respected by both parties involved.

As the pup (Steve called him George) grew older Fred was allowed to inspect and even babysit for a time while Charlie resumed her neglected duties on the hill for ever increasing periods. John didn't want a dog so George went to a farmer's wife who had always longed for a Yorkshire terrier and proved it by driving thirty odd miles to see him when she heard he was for sale. Jean took to the lady immediately and, within half an hour of her arrival, George was on his way to a new home accompanied by a few stifled sobs from Steve and the occasional sniff from Jean.

Charlie couldn't have cared less. She and Fred were busy trying to knock hell out of each other on the back lawn. Fred just about won on points and then they both came in for a drink of water and went to sleep side by side.

We were back to two dogs again and John would have to wait at least another six months for his much wanted Yorkshire bitch.

* * *

"Hey," said Jean beckoning me, "would you believe it? There's another one." I peered into Charlie's whelping box at the five little squirming bodies, and at Charlie busying herself adding another pup to the litter.

It was eight months later and this time Charlie had

well and truly 'clicked'. All the pups were healthy, three dogs and three bitches and John had his pick of the litter. A breeder friend inspected them and picked out one as potentially the best, so that went to John. He called her Jeannie, in deference to Jean I think, but I rather thought that a tradition had been broken and suggested that Bert or Clarence might have been more appropriate. However, I was shouted down and, as it wasn't my dog anyway, I didn't have much say in the matter. I think Jean was quite flattered really.

The puppies stayed with Charlie for nine weeks and then went to their new homes. There was one rather super little dog we kept for a while and Jean began to have great hopes for him. Steve called him Tinker and eventually he went to our friend who is a registered breeder and she had high hopes for him too. I had rather mixed feelings as, if he was good enough, he was destined for the show ring and I like dogs to be dogs, but perhaps I'm being a little unfair. After all, he would have the best of care and attention.

We saw quite a lot of Jeannie, of course, and still do for that matter. Fred taught her how to fight and Charlie taught her hill watching and general lookout duties. Of course, there was Ben to be considered. When he was first introduced to Jeannie he wasn't sure whether it was a dog or his breakfast, she was so small. Dear, gentle Ben; he took her under his wing (or paw) and played with her, tolerating all her puppy antics with the goodwill and forbearance that only the really secure and confident can show. She received the occasional nip when she tried to steal his food for she had inherited the vacuum cleaner approach from her grandmother, but otherwise they all got along famously.

John was very fair with both of them, favouring neither one nor the other but, although Jeannie soon learned that she could charm John into doing almost anything for her, I have a sneaking feeling that Ben just has the slight edge in John's affections. Fred illustrated her recovery by joining in the four cornered tussles that developed whenever John and his dogs visited but, although Ben did his share of barking and tail wagging, one could not help but feel that he felt he was indulging the whims of lesser creatures.

John became an avid reader of any literature concerning Yorkshire terriers and carefully listened to all the advice which was offered. It was typical of him that he sifted out the good from the bad and, for the most part, leant on the experience which we had accumulated since we had adopted Fred. John had said that he wanted to breed from Jeannie and we were pleased that he would be spared the blind groping through ignorance which had been our lot with Fred. Of course, Jeannie was nowhere near the age when she could have pups, but John believed in accumulating as much knowledge as he could in preparation.

That winter there was much planning done late into the night around the fire, this time with John excitedly joining in, now being a member of the 'Yorkie' club. If thoughts and propositions had been reality, Jeannie would have had at least ten litters by the spring. So it is perhaps as well that time and hard work is needed to turn dreams into reality.

That Christmas everyone had a high old time, including the dogs who were deeply preoccupied with a competition which stretched over three of four days. The object was to cram as much food down as possible, the same to be obtained either by begging or stealing. At the end of the day, bellies swollen and utterly exhausted, an honourable draw was declared, the contest to be resumed the following morning. Ben had a slight advantage, being bigger than the others, and distinguished himself by swallowing the head of a five pound brown trout in one gulp and then anxiously looking round for the tail. Jeannie and Fred attacked the mince pies with a ferocity which astonished while Charlie, in her ladylike manner of course, accepted all the trout, pork and turkey which was offered and some, I am afraid to say, which was not.

Everyone seemed to be waiting for the dogs to show the symptoms of excess so recognisable in humans after bouts of gluttony. The waiting was in vain. In between eating and sleeping they showed no signs of stress or discomfort, which is more than can be said for the human beings who attended our Christmas gathering. Perhaps there is a moral to be had in the fact that the dogs took plenty of exercise and not one drop of alcohol passed their lips. They may have put on a little weight but this was soon taken off, as Jean and John imposed a fairly strict diet on them for a week or so following the celebrations.

The winter was mild with only two days of snow (much to Stephen's disgust and our relief), so Fred and Charlie were able to spend much of the daytime outdoors either at home or on their weekday visits to Joan's. When it rained Fred would poke her nose around the kitchen door to watch Charlie sitting on her hill soaked to the skin. Charlie reluctantly came in to be towelled dry when ordered to do so by Jean but, no matter what the weather, she would always make her rounds of the garden late at night, pausing at the hill to gaze in the direction of the cliffs.

I believe Fred thinks Charlie is some sort of idiot.

18

The Back Leg

In the spring, the young man's fancy lightly turns to thoughts of cricket, or so they say. Jean's thoughts turned to puppies. Not Fred's puppies, of course. Not even Charlie's. Now it was Jeannie who was the centre of attention.

Jean began to prepare the way by, once again, drawing attention to Fred's age.

"She's eleven years old now," she sighed. "It's a good age, we can't hope for her to live forever, you know." I remained silent.

"Is Fred going to die?" asked Stephen worriedly.

"Er, well," started Jean, knowing she was well and truly trapped. "Not yet… we hope," she added, glaring at me as I sniggered behind the newspaper. Fred hardly helped Jean's argument by seizing Charlie by the hind legs and attempting to drag her daughter into an impromptu fight.

"Well, what are we talking about then?" demanded Steve, looking at me as I lowered the paper. The fight had started up under the television set and progressed to the kitchen via the back of the settee with Fred doing the chasing and Charlie putting up stubborn resistance.

"Your mother thinks Fred's ready for the knacker's yard," I explained, amid the excited yelping and snarling from the kitchen.

"Don't be crude," said Jean, "and anyway it's not that, it's just... well..."

Steve went to the door of the kitchen and began to give a running commentary on the action. He rather fancied his chances, perhaps it's through watching too much sport on television...

"And it's Fred on top with a back leg hold, but Charlie is fighting back with two quick ear nips followed by a collar grab."

This is a favourite tactic of Charlie's. Unable to match her mother's superior fighting skill, she had grabbed Fred's collar and now, being a larger dog than Fred, used her weight as she lay down on the floor rendering her adversary virtually helpless. Fred is very vulnerable to this move as, although Charlie's tactics are limited, she can be decidedly sneaky at times. Steve returned to the fireside.

"She looks O.K. to me, Dad."

"Fred or your mother?" I inquired. He waited for a moment,

"They both look O.K., except that Mum seems to be seething about something." Stone-faced, Jean bent to her knitting, needles clicking furiously. I forgot to mention that Jean is a dab hand at knitting, cardigans and sweaters mostly. Any enquiries for quotes may be made to the address at the front of this book.

"Well, my old pal," I began, looking at Stephen, "it's something like this, as you will no doubt find out later in life, when a woman wants something she never asks outright for it. She always starts to talk about something else first, usually something loosely connected with what she wants in the first place. On the other hand it may have no connection whatever. It's a preliminary exercise to get the vocal chords working."

"But that's silly, if you want something... you... "

"Ahh,"I interrupted, "quite right, but you're not a woman you see. You think logically." Jean glared at us and remained silent as, filled with unholy glee, I continued to prepare my son for the brain-smashing encounters that I hoped he would experience as he grew older. "The way it works is this," I went on, "when they (here I nodded at Jean, who was going puce in the face) want something, they will try and make you believe that it was your idea. This is why all the talk about other things comes first."

"Why?" asked Steve.

"So that if anything goes wrong, or things don't quite work out, they can say it's not their fault as it was your idea in the first place," I finished triumphantly.

"Are they all like that?" inquired Steve.

"Every one," I replied. "That's what makes them so smashing."

"Is that why you love Mum?"

"In a way, yes. That and a lot of other things."

"You're barmy, and I think Mum's going to explode," he said, glancing at his mother.

Jean did, but with laughter.

"Stephen," she called. "You can tell your father that he and his dog are a right pair of let downs." (When Fred does not conform to Jean's wishes she is always my dog).

"Well, what *do* you want, Mum?"

"I would like," said Jean slowly, grinning at me, "another little Yorkie to take Fred's place when she eventually… " Here she was interrupted as her feet were knocked aside by the flying figure of Fred who, now having released herself from the collar hold, was at full tilt after Charlie in a mad chase around the house. Steve sniggered, Jean glared again and I went to fetch some more wood for the fire. It was a beautiful spring evening but a little warmth never went amiss anywhere.

* * *

"You had better ask John," I said the following day.

"Yes, I know," replied Jean. "Anyway," she continued, "I don't really think she ought to pup yet. I suppose I got a bit carried away, but I would like to keep on the strain. Anyway, it was only a tentative enquiry as to what you feel about it."

Since we were married Jean and I have always made our decisions together, I don't remember either of us ever doing anything even remotely important without consulting the other. So together we decided that, when the right pup came and the right time came, we would have another Yorkie bitch – always provided that Jeannie would oblige.

Whether or not Jeannie would oblige was a moot point. Encouraged no doubt by Ben, she was rapidly becoming the Bodecea of Rossell Drive. With the guts of Fred and the build of Charlie, she feared nothing and it seemed that her destiny lay in leading an army of similarly disposed Yorkshire terriers to right all the wrongs which have been done to the breed in the name of fashion. Not for Jeannie the carefully groomed and beribboned pomp and posturing of the show ring. Hers is a world of food and fights, with swashbuckling good humour and a great zest for life.

"She ought to have been a bloody pirate," observed John one night as Jeannie, having had her titbits, was trying to rob the other three dogs of their share. She didn't get much satisfaction from Fred or Charlie but gentle Ben, playing the indulgent philanthropist, allowed her a small morsel of his cake. I think that, because of her size, Ben still regards Jeannie as a baby collie and must be constantly puzzled as to why she never grows up. John, Jean and I talked about a pup long into that night and it was decided that we wait six months or so to find her a mate and see how she reacted.

"How do you think she will behave?" Jean asked, glancing at John.

"I think," said John reflectively, "that she will go for the back leg."

19

Fighting Fit

Six months have passed since we talked about having a puppy. We have just returned from a holiday in the Yorkshire Dales where Stephen distinguished himself by falling in the River Ure on our first day there and having to walk a mile back to the car, still soaked to the skin. Steve didn't seem to mind at all, but Jean muttered ominously all the way back. That apart, we had a great time. We didn't take the dogs. Fred and Charlie stayed with Joan and, from all accounts, had a whale of a time being taken for walks and generally being over-indulged.

I don't really think hotels suit Fred any more. As she gets older her eyesight deteriorates and she is not as nippy at dodging feet in crowded places as she was. Her hearing and sense of smell seem to be as good as ever and she has an extra pair of eyes in Charlie. The two of them are rarely apart these days.

Fred is by no means finished, however. A few weeks ago she got into a fight with a Jack Russell late one night.

We were about to go to bed when strange noises began coming from the back garden. I opened the kitchen door and saw the Jack pulling something from a plastic bag of kitchen refuse outside the door. The plastic had been torn open and the dog was nosing around in the rubbish, strewing it all over the place. The reason the plastic bag was there was because somebody had pinched our dustbin. They'll pinch anything around our way if it's not nailed down. The dogs were out before I could stop them; Charlie in the lead. She bundled into the Jack, closely followed by Fred, as Jean and I rushed out to separate them, Jean's vocabulary becoming highly coloured as she gave forth about people who let their dogs roam around at night.

Fred followed hard on Charlie's heels and dived in. Now, as I said a little earlier, Fred's eyesight is not as it was, and it was dark. Not being too particular, the first thing Fred grabbed was Charlie's back leg. Charlie yelled in pain, anger and indignation, let go of the Jack and retreated to watch her mother sail into the attack, Fred now having made sure of her target. The Jack grabbed Fred by the ear and I don't care to mention where Fred's teeth took hold. Suffice to say that it makes your eyes water and brings colour to your cheeks. We weren't exactly standing around doing nothing, but the whole performance took only about five seconds before I parted them, none too gently, I might add. The Jack Russell shot off through the fence and, after Jean had cleaned up the mess, we all retreated to the house.

We have a new dustbin now.

Fred dripped blood on the kitchen floor but seemed quite unconcerned by the incident. Charlie came in, after a few quick victory laps of the garden, as we examined the protesting Fred. Two neat holes pierced her left ear where it had been bitten clean through. After a quick sponge with warm water and disinfectant, the bleeding soon stopped and Fred seemed quite indignant about all the fuss that was being made. Next morning she was as good as new but the Jack Russell hasn't visited since.

Jean has just reminded me of the telephone call we had while on holiday. Jeannie was mated while we were away so we'll just have to wait and see what happens. Even if she has a litter I don't think we will have one of them yet as Fred is still so active.

The parvo virus has hit our area. I spent yesterday improving the fencing round the garden and putting a new closing spring on the gate in an attempt to keep Fred and Charlie in and, hopefully, other dogs out. A friend of Jean's, who had one of Charlie's pups, rang to say that it had contracted the disease at boarding kennels while they were away on holiday. The kennels have closed down now and many of the dogs boarded have died. The vet seems to think that Pat's dog will recover but she says the symptoms are horrible.

Today Jean rang our vet and, within a couple of hours, Fred and Charlie had been vaccinated. It's not the proper vaccination (there isn't one yet) but he says it will help, should they come in contact with the disease. So we can only hope and keep them at home and out of the company of other dogs.

I often think back to the day of the wedding when I agreed to have Fred. It seems so long ago and I can't imagine being without the dogs now. I know Fred can't live forever but we have Charlie, and who knows what Jeannie will produce, as Fred's line will, hopefully, be carried on.

Sometimes it is the small things in life that bring so much happiness. The love, trust and friendship that Fred gives to us and to me in particular, who was so indifferent to dogs, is beyond price. Jean insists that Fred is really my dog and that I should call this book 'My Girl Fred', but I think I will settle for 'A Girl Called Fred'. The companionship and humour mixed, at times, with frustration and concern that she has brought to our home is for all of us.

One of my favourite hymns begins 'God moves in a mysterious way, His wonders to perform'. He certainly moved in a mysterious way at that wedding when he presented us with a scruffy little dog from Yorkshire that has brought us such joy and – sheer fun.

It's getting dark now as I finish these last few lines. John has called and he, Jean and Steve are playing cards on the coffee table. Steve is having difficulty distinguishing between clubs and spades, or so he says, and the game is interrupted by howls of protestation and injured innocence. I thought I heard the word 'cheat' just then.

The dogs are quietly asleep by Jean's side, undisturbed by the racket.

I took a walk outside a few minutes ago and, by the look of the clouds, I think it might rain tomorrow. I'm glad I mowed the lawn today. I bet Fred is too.

She hates tiddling in long wet grass.

Acknowledgements

The two years after Roger died were the worst of my life. Then, after thirty years of gathering dust, I found his manuscript. Reading it again was an emotional experience and brought back many good memories. I decided to try to get it published. I am grateful to all the staff at Matador for helping me to do so.

The illustrations were drawn by Anne Eley. Thank you Anne and, if you see this, please get in touch. I have been trying to find you for some time.

To Jenny Price; for your friendship and editing skills, Jenny, you have my gratitude. I couldn't have done it without you.

To my new friends at Beeston U3A, especially Breda, Zena and Marie, thank you for your support.

Heartfelt thanks to my cousins, Stephen and Christine, and to my friends, Fiona and Nick, who gave me so much encouragement. Thanks also to John, Ann and all the members of our Book Group.

My gratitude and love go to my dearest friend Pat and her family; Denis, Sarah, Patrick, Stuart and Victoria. I would not have survived Roger's death without them in my life. Their love and support is invaluable.

Finally, Roger would want me to pay tribute to our son, Steve, who bought such joy into our lives and to all our dogs past and present; the Yorkies, Fred and Charlie; the Collies, Ru and Meg and our beautiful Golden Retriever, Jack. We loved them all, but Fred was our first dog – the special one.

Jean Willgoose 2014

Born in 1935, Roger lived in Trowell near Nottingham until he married Jean in 1968 when they settled in Stapleford. He attended Trowell Infants School and Ilkeston Grammar School until he joined the Nottingham Evening Post in 1952 as a commercial artist. After 2 years National Service in the RAF, where he learned aerial photography, he returned to the Post, qualified as a Press Photographer and continued in that role for the next 37 years. He loved taking pictures for the sports department, especially football, and he was an avid supporter of Derby County.

Never having owned a pet, Roger was not happy with the prospect of suddenly adopting a Yorkshire terrier. His anxieties were soon to be dispelled by the feisty young dog and the bond that developed between them produced this book in 1981. The manuscript was gifted to Jean but after several rejections by publishers it was 'mislaid', only to be discovered in 2013, three years after Roger's death.